Electrical Phenomena
in Gases

Electrical Phenomena
in Gases

R. PAPOULAR

Translated by B. JEFFREY
Edited by Dr. D. L. JONES
King's College, London

LONDON   ILIFFE BOOKS LTD
NEW YORK   AMERICAN ELSEVIER PUBLISHING
COMPANY INC.

English translation © Iliffe Books Ltd 1965
First published in France in 1963 by
Dunod, Éditeur, under the title
Les Phénomènes Electriques dans les Gaz

Translated and prepared for press by
Scripta Technica Ltd

Printed and bound in England by
Butler & Tanner Ltd
Frome and London
BKS 5077

Published in the U.S.A. by
American Elsevier Publishing Company Inc.
52 Vanderbilt Avenue, New York, N.Y. 10017
Library of Congress Catalogue Card Number 65-23110

contents

preface to the french edition

The passage of an electric current through a gas is accompanied by a surprising luminous emission which is at once brilliant, colored and cold. These colors have fascinated observers ever since their discovery at the very beginnings of the systematic study of electricity. Thus, in the nineteenth century, many very eminent physicists devoted themselves to investigating the mechanism of discharge tubes. Their efforts have been rewarded, if only indirectly, by many interesting discoveries which often appear now to be very far removed from the original field of research. Thus cathode rays and X-rays were first created in discharge tubes and cosmic rays were discovered during a patient study of the electrical conductivity of the atmosphere. Meanwhile the discharge itself turned out to be a more and more complex phenomenon and the way in which it functioned remained a mystery. Towards 1910, J. J. Thomson gave a masterly summary of the results acquired up to that time, but even at this time explanation often gave way to description. In the twentieth century the pace of research accelerated. Engineers became interested in discharge tubes and plasmas and introduced them into everyday life in the form of domestic fluorescent lighting and neon signs. In addition, longwave radio communication depends on the varying properties of the ionosphere (a natural plasma) as well as on radio engineering techniques, thus again illustrating the influence of plasmas on everyday life.

Today success in producing controlled nuclear reactions has widened yet further the horizons and ambitions of scientists and engineers. Nuclear reactors which depend on the fission of solid uranium have brought about a revolutionary progress in our conception of energy sources, and they have had so great an impact both with the general public and with research workers and politicians that an investigation of "fusion" reactors is now contemplated. These studies involve the use of an extremely large discharge tube¹ and employ an inexhaustible source of fuel, since this fuel is hydrogen or one of its isotopes. With the help of Euratom, France has already initiated several "fusion" projects on a commercial basis, thus providing numerous opportunities for scientists.

It is with great pleasure that I present this work by one of these scientists, Mr. Papoular. Drawing on the results of brilliant teaching experiments with his young colleagues, he has applied himself to the problems of teaching these important developments. He gives a clear and precise picture of the elementary processes involved in discharges as known today.

These basic processes can only be elucidated thanks to the progressive accumulation of precise and original methods of measurement which make use of very disparate techniques: Langmuir probes, high frequency conductivity, refraction of millimeter waves, emission and absorption spectroscopy. Here again this book makes an original and significant contribution in giving a modern and coherent review of "diagnostic" methods for plasmas. The contents have already received an enthusiastic welcome from the students of the 3rd course of higher electronics in the Faculty of Sciences in Paris. The author has made certain improvements in the text: its high quality and excellent production in the Dunod editions should assure its success with a vast public of students and young research workers interested in the problems posed by wave propagation in ionized media, the development of gas discharge tubes and controlled thermonuclear reactions.

Pierre GRIVET
Professor of the Faculty of
Sciences at the University
of Paris

preface to the english edition

This translation of Mr. R. Papoular's monograph from the original French edition should be of value to those engaged in research in the fields of basic plasma physics and gaseous discharges as well as to undergraduates specializing in physics, chemistry and electrical and electronic engineering. This wide appeal has been achieved by outlining the development of the necessary concepts from first principles to the forefront of present-day research. Although some preparation in mathematics is assumed, the author is always concerned with the physical principles of the processes involved and no one should have any difficulty in following the development of the theme. The style is brief, precise and to the point, making the text eminently suitable for reference purposes. Basic reactions among subatomic, atomic and molecular particles are treated in detail as is the derivation of the macroscopic characteristics of the gas from microscopic parameters. The addition of a section on plasma diagnostics which includes the theory of the Langmuir probe and an outline of microwave methods is significant in this space age in which satellite observations have demonstrated the dominance of plasma processes in the universe. The author strikes a happy balance between theory and experiment throughout, much recent experimental data being included to illustrate the text. An index has been added to this English edition, thus further increasing the value of the book as a work of reference.

D. Llanwyn Jones, B.Sc., Ph.D.
September 1964

1 review of concepts of structure of matter. spectroscopy

1.1 General description of matter

An atom is constructed of electrons circulating around a nucleus.

1.1.1 Description of an electron

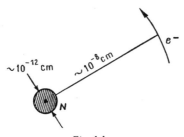

Fig. 1.1

diameter 4×10^{-13} cm
rest mass $m_e = 9.1 \times 10^{-28}$ gm
electric charge $-e = -1.6 \times 10^{-19}$ C
                       $= -4.8 \times 10^{-10}$ CGS ESU
tangential velocity $\Big\}$ $\approx c/100$
frequency of rotation $\Big\}$ for hydrogen $\approx 10^{16}$ c/s
distance from nucleus $\Big\}$ $a_0 \approx 10^{-8}$ cm

1

1.1.2 Description of the nucleus

The nucleus is composed of nucleons having the following characteristics:

protons
$\begin{cases}
\text{electric charge} & e = 1.6 \times 10^{-19} \text{ C} \\
\text{rest mass} & m_p = 1.672 \times 10^{-24} \text{ gm} \\
 & = 1.836 \, m_e \\
\text{atomic mass} & (= Nm_p, \text{ where } N = \text{Avogadro's number} \\
 & = 6.024 \times 10^{23}) = 1.00758 \text{ AMU (atomic mass units)}
\end{cases}$

neutrons
$\begin{cases}
\text{electric charge} & e \\
\text{rest mass} & m_n = 1.675 \times 10^{-24} \text{ gm} \\
\text{atomic mass} & \quad\; 1.00894 \text{ AMU}
\end{cases}$

It is important to note that nucleons have dimensions of the same order of magnitude as those of electrons.

In an atom with atomic number Z, in the normal (unexcited) state, there are:

Z protons and Z electrons,

N neutrons (in general $N \geqslant Z$ for stable atoms, i.e., those which do not disintegrate spontaneously).

The total number $M = N + Z$ is called the mass number and is very close to the atomic weight.

Example: Hydrogen $Z = 1, N = 0, M = 1$
　　　　　Oxygen　　$Z = 8, N = 8, M = 16$

The dimensions of a nucleus are of the order of 10^{-12} cm; theory gives for the nuclear radius

$$R \approx 1.5 \times 10^{-13} M^{1/3} \text{ cm}$$

1.1.3

Thus the greater part of the space occupied by an atom is empty; at intervals in this space are found particles 10^5 smaller than the whole. This explains the great power of penetration of neutrons into matter; they cannot be deflected except by a collision with a proton or a neutron.

In the following only the nuclear parameters Z or M are involved. These two parameters determine the electrical, mechanical, chemical and optical properties of atoms.

1.1.4

A molecule is an assembly of atoms bound together. Even in elementary substances (hydrogen, oxygen, etc.), this is the form in which atoms are most frequently found.

A molecule of a substance X will be designated by the symbol

$$\underset{Z}{\overset{M}{}} X \overset{\pm i}{\underset{j}{}}$$

where
i = degree of ionization = number of extra or missing electrons
j = number of bound electrons

The dimensions of a molecule are still of the order of 10^{-8} cm (those of an atom) since the constituent atoms penetrate into one another (atoms are just empty space!).

Let us now return to the atom to study the constitution of the electron cloud circulating round the nucleus.

1.2 Quantum numbers and atomic structure

To a first approximation, the trajectory of an electron is determined only by the nucleus (charge and mass) and the electron itself; the other electrons have no influence. Thus the trajectory is an ellipse if it is assumed that the electron does not emit radiation during the course of its gravitation (centripetal acceleration).

Now quantum mechanics shows that this is only true for a discrete number of orbits: the orbits are said to be "quantized."

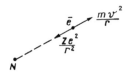

The solution to the equations of quantum mechanics shows that these allowed orbits depend, in general, on 3 quantum numbers.

n: the principal quantum number; 1, 2, 3—a positive integer; roughly defines the total energy of the electron and its mean distance from the nucleus.

l: the orbital or azimuthal quantum number: 0, 1 ... $n-1$ (n values); roughly defines the eccentricity and the angular momentum (constant) of the electron:

$$| G | = \sqrt{l(l+1)}\, \hbar$$

$\hbar = h/2\pi$ is the quantum of action; this constant has the dimensions of action (energy × time); h is Planck's constant (6.6×10^{-27} erg·sec) and $\hbar$ is a reduced form of Planck's constant.

The eccentricity of the orbit increases with l (see Fig. 1.2). Generally the states l = 0, 1, 2, 3 are designated by s, p, d, f, respectively.

m : the magnetic quantum number = $-1, -(l-1), \ldots -1, 0, 1 \ldots l$ ($2l + 1$ values) defines the orientation of the orbit and the projection of **G** on the chosen axis Oz

$$G_z = m\hbar$$

(see Fig. 1.3).

To define an electron gravitating about a nucleus completely a fourth quantum number must be introduced.

s : the spin quantum number = $\tfrac{1}{2}$ (a single value) defines the angular momentum of the electron itself (i.e., the spin angular momentum of a charge of finite dimensions)

$$|\mathbf{g}| = \sqrt{s(s + 1)}\, \hbar$$

This vector can only be parallel or antiparallel to **G** (i.e., there are two possible orientations).

The projection of this vector on $Oz = g_z = \pm s\hbar = \pm \hbar/2$.

Fig. 1.2   Fig. 1.3

Conclusion. Four quantum numbers are necessary to define the properties of the electron: n, l, m, s.

Instead of m and s one can describe the electron in terms of:

j (total angular momentum quantum number) = $(l \pm s) = (l \pm \tfrac{1}{2})$ which in a way defines the total angular momentum, orbital + spin; and

m_j (magnetic angular momentum quantum number) = $m \pm \tfrac{1}{2} = -j$, $-j + 1, \ldots, j - 1, j$.

In general, that is to say, in the presence of an electric or magnetic field (which destroys the isotropy of space), the state, and hence the energy, of an electron is determined by the four quantum numbers given above. The energy of the electron is said to be "quantized."

The allowed values of the energy, the *energy levels*, are discrete and are distributed as shown in the following diagram (see Fig. 1.4) where each of the horizontal lines on the extreme right represents an energy level of an electron. The energy level can be found from the vertical axis on the left, calibrated with reference to the line (0) which is the energy of a free electron at rest. The density of levels increases with n. For a given value of n, the levels are approximately:

$$E_n = -\frac{m_e e^4}{2h^2}\frac{Z^2}{n^2} \quad \text{(CGS ESU)}$$

(We may note that this is the expression for the sum of the kinetic and potential energies of a negative electron $(-e)$ moving in a circular orbit about a nucleus at the center, the radius of the orbit being such that the centrifugal force is equal and opposite to the electrostatic attractive force of the positive nucleus (Ze).)

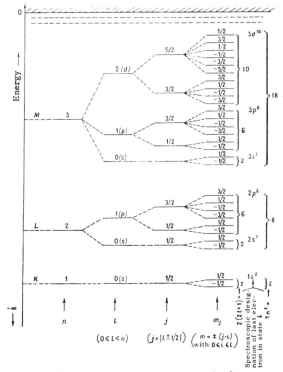

Fig. 1.4. General diagram of energy levels

Naturally the exact magnitudes of the energy levels depend on the nuclear species and on the number of electrons present.

However, it is possible to state some useful general rules:

The H atom (normal state) is made up of a proton $(Z = M = 1)$ and an electron in the lowest possible energy state $(1, 0, 0, \pm \frac{1}{2})$.

Each time that a step is taken in the direction of increasing atomic number Z in the Periodic Table of the elements (Mendeleev's table), the nucleon complement of the nucleus is increased by one proton (and by a certain number of neutrons), while the cloud of electrons is increased by one electron which takes up its position in the least energetic unoccupied level in Fig. 1.4.

The electrons with the same n form a "shell" (K, L ... Z shells). Within an atom it is impossible for two electrons to exist in the same state, that is to say, to be characterized by the same four quantum numbers. This is the Pauli exclusion principle. Thus, merely by studying the possible combinations of the four quantum numbers, all the simple natural substances may be described (see Table 1.1).

Table 1.1. Configuration of electron cloud

Elements	Z	Shell		
		K	L	M
H	1	$1s$		
He	2	$1s^2$		
Li	3	$1s^2$	$2s$	
Ne	10	$1s^2$	$2s^2 2p^6$	
Na	11	$1s^2$	$2s^2 2p^6$	$3s$

It has been shown that:

(a) It is essentially the electrons in the outermost shell which determine the spectroscopic and chemical properties of simple substances: these are called the valence electrons.

(b) Atoms in which the outermost shell is complete (saturated) are chemically inert (the rare gases).

(c) Atoms in which the outermost shells have the same configuration have analogous spectroscopic and chemical properties.

1.3 Excited states of the atom: spectral lines

These observations, together with quantum theory, have led to the following explanation of optical spectra:

Let us consider an atom ${}_Z^M X_1^0$ made up in the normal way in accordance with the rules given above; the Z electrons in the cloud occupy the lowest possible levels between the ground level ($n = 1$, $l = 0$, $m = 0$) and a particular higher level determined by the value of Z. The atom is said to be in the *ground state*. This state is determined by the shape of the outer shell of valence electrons, that is to say (at least for light atoms), by the number of the shell n, by the orbital quantum number L which is the vector sum of the orbital momenta $L = \Sigma l$, and finally by the angular momentum quantum number J which characterizes the total angular momentum $J = L + S$, where $S = \Sigma s$. Only the valence electrons enter into these vector sums since the corresponding summation for completed inner shells is zero. The state in question is represented by the symbol

$$n^r L_J$$

where r = multiplicity = number of possible values for J.

The energy, E_1, of the system is called the energy of the atom in its ground state.

Now, if there is an external perturbation (collision, irradiation, etc.), one or more valence electrons may change their states, thus modifying the state of the atom itself and raising it to a higher energy level, E_n. The atom is then excited. This transformation, or transition, is, of course, accompanied by the absorption of a quantum of energy (photon or mechanical, electrical or magnetic energy):

$$h\nu = E_n - E_1$$

Conversely, the return of the atom to the normal ground state is accompanied by a loss in internal energy, this being transformed into a quantum of radiation $h\nu$. In general:

$$h\nu_{jk} = E_j - E_k \quad \text{(Ritz combination principle)}$$

the energies $E_{j,k}$ are called spectral terms.

Each spectral line results from the combination of two spectral terms.

Unit: $1 \text{ eV} = 1.6 \times 10^{-12} \text{ ergs}$.

For $E = 1 \text{ eV}$, $\nu = 2.5 \times 10^{14} \text{ c/s}$, $\lambda \approx 1\mu$.

Wave number = $1/\lambda$ (cm^{-1}) = $\nu/c = 10^4 \text{ cm}^{-1}$.

In the equation above j and k cannot have every possible value; there are selection rules which must be obeyed in the transition

$$\Delta L = \pm 1 ; \quad \Delta J = 0 \text{ or } \pm 1$$
$$\hookrightarrow \text{excepting } J = 0$$

This rule is not absolutely obeyed:

—in the case where the above conditions are fulfilled, the return to the ground state takes place in 10^{-8} to 10^{-7} sec;

—in other cases (metastable states), it can last up to 10^{-2} sec after which there is a transition to a higher level (important in rare gases), excitation of another atom or electron or emission of an electron.

When an excited atom returns directly to the initial level (from which it was excited) resonance is said to occur.

If the energy absorbed by the atom is sufficient, an electron may be stripped from the cloud: the atom is then ionized (cf. photo-electric effect).

B

The ionization energy, E_i, is that energy which it is necessary to supply to remove the electron to infinity. It is larger the deeper the shell to which the electron belongs. The smallest of these energies, E_{i1}, is called the first ionization energy related to the first ionization potential V_{i1} by $V_{i1} = E_{i1}/e$. First ionization potentials (critical potentials) for various atoms are shown in Table 1.2.

Table 1.2. Critical potentials for various atoms

V_m = metastable level; V_r = resonance level; V_{i1}, V_{ir}.... successive ionization potentials. All in electron volts (eV)

Element	V_m	V_r	V_{i1}	V_{i2}	V_{i3}
H......		10.2	13.6		
He.....	19.8	21.2	24.6	54.4	
C......	1.26	7.5	11.3	24.4	47.9
N......	2.38	10.3	14.5	29.6	47.4
O......	1.97	9.2	13.6	35.2	54.9
Hg.....	4.7	4.9	10.4	18.7	34.2

The general form of the variation of V_{i1} as a function of the atomic number Z is shown in Fig. 1.5. From this it can be seen that V_{i1} increases from the first to the last element on the same line of the periodic table; with the rare gases, V_{i1} decreases as Z increases: these are general, but not rigorous, rules.

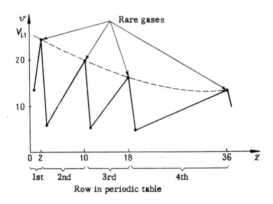

Fig. 1.5. General nature of the variations in the first ionization potential as a function of atomic number

Table 1.2 also shows that V_{i1} is of the order of 10 v while the successive ionization potentials increase rapidly with order; they may reach kilovolts for heavy elements.

The inverse phenomenon to photoelectric ionization is radiative recombination, whereby an ionized atom recaptures an electron which integrates with the electron cloud to form the initial, normal atom; in the course of this operation the atom loses energy E_i (= binding energy of an electron = ionization energy of the same electron) in the form of a photon of frequency $\nu = E_i/h$.

If an isolated electron e^- initially has a kinetic energy E (non-quantized), then $\nu = (E_i + E)/h$ (continuous spectrum).

1.4 Application to the simple case of H(Z = 1)

One single electron: 1 s state. Thus

$$\left. \begin{array}{ll} L = 1 \text{ and } L = l = 0 \\ S = s \qquad\quad S = s = 1/2 \end{array} \right\} J = S = 1/2$$

and the symbol for the ground state will be $1\ ^1S_{1/2}$.

In this case, the only part of the internal energy of the atom of interest to us is the energy of the electron. But we have seen that the corresponding terms were of the form:

$$E_n = -\frac{m_e e^4}{2\hbar^2} \cdot \frac{1}{n^2} \quad \text{(dependent only on } n)$$

The wave numbers of the lines will therefore be of the form:

$$\nu_{jk} = R_0 \left(\frac{1}{n_j^2} - \frac{1}{n_k^2} \right)$$

where

$$R_0 = \text{Rydberg's constant} = \frac{2\pi^2 m_e e^4}{ch^3} = 109{,}737 \text{ cm}^{-1}$$

See the diagrammatic representation in Fig. 1.6.

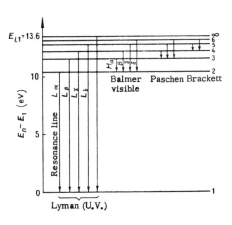

Fig. 1.6. Diagram of the energy levels and the spectrum lines of atomic hydrogen. The lines are grouped in series according to the final level and each series is named after its discoverer. E_{i_1} is the maximum energy that an atom can emit in the form of a photon (during radiative recombination)

1.5 Analogous spectra

1. Those of the alkaline metals. These have a single valence electron. The two electrons in the K skell interact, thus multiplying the levels corresponding to each quantum number n. Thus terms depending on quantum numbers l and j appear giving rise to fine structure, these terms being designated by nL_J. In a general way, the spectral terms, which were of the form R_0/n^2 for hydrogen, will have the form:

$$T_k = \frac{R'_0}{(\eta + \alpha)^2}$$

where

R'_0 = modified Rydberg constant which takes into account the particular mass of the nucleus in question;

α = correction depending on l and j.

The T_k terms are generally designated by the symbols nS_j, nP_j, nD_j, nF_j. The spectral lines are written:

$$nS - mP$$
$$\text{(low) (high)}$$

2. Spectra of atoms ionized in such a way that only one electron remains circling the nucleus, e.g., He^{+1}, Li^{+2}, Be^{+3}, etc. The spectral terms are then in the form

$$T_k = \frac{R'_0 Z^2}{(\eta + \alpha)^2}$$

where Z = atomic number.

3. In general:

(a) the spectra of atoms in the same column in the periodic table are analogous,

(b) the spectrum of a neutral (nonionized) atom with atomic number Z is analogous to an atom F times ionized with atomic number $Z + F$.

Remarks: In spectroscopy, a neutral atom is designated by A I, a singly ionized atom by A II, etc. A I spectra are usually obtained using arcs or flames. A II spectra are usually obtained using sparks.

Absorption spectra consist of the same wavelengths as emission spectra.

In the presence of B or E (magnetic or electric fields), the spectra become more complicated because of the multiplicity of levels. These phenomena are known as the Zeeman and Stark effects respectively.

1.6 Other spectra

Molecules. Here again the wave numbers are given by different spectral terms the values of which represent the energy of a specific state of the molecule. But in this case the energy is not only that of one or more electrons; the energies of the different constituent atoms must be taken into account. This energy is connected with the motion of the atoms, e.g., rotational and vibrational motions (see Fig. 1.7).

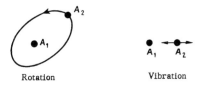

Rotation   Vibration

Fig. 1.7

In this case band spectra (i.e., several adjacent equidistant lines) are obtained in the infrared and microwave regions of the spectrum. The excitation energy is much lower than for atomic spectra (~ 1 ev).

It is also necessary to take into account the modified spectra of the constituent atoms.

Table 1.3. Critical potentials of various molecules (in volts)

V_d = dissociation potential; V_{i1} = ionization potential $(M_2 \to M_2^+ + e^-$ or $AB \to AB^+ + e^-)$

Molecule	V_d	V_{i1}
H_2	4.5	15.6
N_2	9.8	15.5
O_2	5.1	12.5
CO_2	16.6	14.4
NO	6.5	9.5

Black body. A sufficiently heated black body will radiate both in the infrared and in the visible, but the wavelengths emitted are so close together that they cannot be distinguished: the spectrum is continuous. The exact process giving rise to the radiation is not known, but it is assumed to be essentially dipole radiation due to the electrons and ions oscillating about their equilibrium positions. However, it is possible to deduce Planck's radiation law without knowing the exact nature of the radiation mechanism. Planck's Law states that

$$E_\lambda = C_1 \lambda^{-5}/[\exp(C_2/\lambda T) - 1]$$

where
   E_λ = the energy of the emitted ratiation per unit of wavelength centered about the wavelength λ;
   T = absolute temperature of body; and C_1, C_2 are universal constants (see Fig. 1.8).

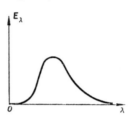

Fig. 1.8. Distribution of
black body radiation

REFERENCES

General

1. BRUHAT, KASTLER, *Optics* (Masson, 1955).
2. GUINIER, *Modern Physics* (Bordas, 1951).
3. BORN, *Atomic Physics* (Blackie and Sons, G. B., 1958).
4. PAULING, *Nature of the Chemical Bond* (Dunod).
5. LAPP and ANDREWS, *Nuclear Radiation Physics* (Prentice Hall, U.S.A., 1949).

Quantum Mechanics

1. MARGENAU and MURPHY, *Mathematics of Physics and Chemistry* (Van Nostrand, U.S.A., 1957), Chs. 8, 9 and 11.
2. MESSIAH, *Quantum Mechanics* (Dunod, 1960).
3. SCHIFF, *Quantum Mechanics* (McGraw-Hill, U.S.A., 1949).
4. M. Y. BERNARD, *Introduction to Quantum Mechanics* (Hachette, 1960).

Numerical Tables

1. HODGMAN, *Handbook of Chemistry and Physics for the Current Year* (Chemical Rubber Publishing Co., U.S.A.).
2. *American Institute of Physics Handbook* (McGraw-Hill, U.S.A., 1957).

2 elementary phenomena and concepts

2.1 Introduction

The molecules of a gas interact only weakly as opposed to those of solids and liquids. For the greater part of their existence they are subject to a uniform, linear motion. But one particle may, from time to time, approach sufficiently close to another, or several others, for their orientations, velocities and even their internal characteristics to be altered. These encounters are called collisions. Despite their rarity it is collisions which dominate gas theory because of their immediate and important consequences: it is the collisions which enable the setting up of thermodynamic equilibrium or a steady state; it is also the collisions which determine the nature and intensity of the radiation emitted by a gas, and the state and distribution of the particles present.

If ions and electrons are present in the gas under investigation, the situation is altered considerably (becoming, of course, more complicated). Firstly, charged particles are influenced by forces which have no effect on molecules or neutral atoms: i.e., forces of electric and magnetic origin, and secondly, the particles themselves produce an electric field with a large range of influence since it decreases with $1/r^2$ (instead of the law characteristic of molecular forces, $1/r^7$). The result is that with the same density of particles, the interactions between particles are more important and the effects of such interactions are more long-lasting. That is why the physics of ionized gases is a great deal more complicated than that of neutral gases.

Table 2.1. Table of elementary processes in gas discharges

Test \ Target	Electromagnetic radiation γ or $h\nu$	Elementary charged particle with no nucleus e^-, p^+, ….	Particle with one nucleus and at least one electron: ion or excited or nonexcited atom	Particle with at least one nucleus and at least one electron: neutral or ionized molecule, excited or nonexcited
Electromagnetic radiation γ or $h\nu$	Materialization $h\nu + h\nu \to e^+ + e^-$	Compton effect $h\nu + e^- \to h\nu + e^-$ Diffusion	Compton effect (e^- ejected) Diffusion Excitation $h\nu + A \to A^*$ (change of energy level) Ionization $h\nu + A \to A^+ + e^-$ (photo-ionization) or $h\nu + A^- \to A + e^-$ (photoelectric detachment)	Compton effect (e^- ejected) Diffusion Excitation $h\nu + AB \to AB^*$ (change of energy level, rotation, vibration) Ionization $h\nu + AB \to AB^+ + e^-$ (photo-ionization) or $h\nu + AB^- \to AB + e^-$ (photoelectric detachment) Dissociation $h\nu + AB \to A + B$
Elementary charged particle or nucleus e^-, p^+, …		Annihilation $e^- + e^+ \to h\nu$ Nuclear reactions Elastic collision	Nuclear reactions Elastic collision Excitation $e^- + A \to A^* + e^-$ Ionization and detachment $e^- + A^* \to A^+ + e^- + e^-$ Collision of 2nd type $e^- + A^* \to A + e^-$ Recombination (a) radiative $e^- + A^+ \searrow A + h\nu,$ $\nearrow A^* + h\nu,$ particular case of attachment $e^- + A \to A^- + h\nu$ (b) 3 body $e^- + A^+ + B \to A + B^-$	Nuclear reactions Elastic collision Excitation $e^- + AB \to AB^* + e^-$ Ionization and detachment $e^- + AB^* \to AB^+ + e^- + e^-$ Collision of 2nd type $e^- + AB^* \to AB + \overline{e}$ Recombination (a) radiative (b) 3 body (c) dissociative $e^- + AB^+ \to A^* + B^*$ Dissociation (with or without excitation or ionization) $e^- + AB \to A + B + e^-$
Ion or atom			All the above reactions. Transfer of charge $\underline{A^+ + B \to A + B^+}$	All the above reactions. Transfer of charge
Molecule				All the above reactions

Nevertheless, a large number of the basic concepts of the theory of ionized gases have been derived from the theory of neutral gases. Thus the terms "impact" and "collision" have been conserved despite the fact that they lose their sense of abruptness and violence in the case of charged particles.

In the following the term "particle" will cover photons as well as particles of matter either charged or uncharged.

Because of the low density of gases, most collisions are binary, that is to say, only two particles are involved; however, there can also be ternary collisions involving three particles.

A differentiation should be made between elastic and inelastic collisions. The first only modify the magnitude and direction of the velocities, while the second can also give rise to changes in internal energy or in the nature of the particles present (mass, charge, etc.), the total kinetic energy being altered in such a way as to conserve the total energy.

The most numerous among the inelastic collisions are those of the first kind: that is to say, part of the kinetic energy of the particles involved is converted into internal energy (endothermic reaction). Conversely, in a collision of the second kind, it is the internal energy which is partially or totally converted into kinetic energy (exothermic reaction). This distinction no longer has any significance if one of the particles is a photon.

2.2 Possible reactions and their products

There are numerous different types of collisions in each of the categories just described. These are classified in Table 2.1 according to the initial nature of the particles in question. The table is not intended to be exhaustive.

In a laboratory system one of the particles, called the "test" particle, generally has a much greater velocity than the other, which is considered to be at rest and is called the "target." This assumption greatly facilitates the calculations but is not always justified. In any event, the same reaction would be obtained by interchanging the roles of the target particle and the test particle. Table 2.1 is therefore symmetric about the diagonal and this explains why only half has been completed. The symbols used represent—

A, B, AB: neutral atoms or molecules in the ground state
$A*, AB*$: neutral atoms or molecules in an excited state
A^+: singly ionized atoms
A^{++}: doubly ionized atoms
A^-: negative ion
$e^\pm$: positron or electron
ν or ν': photon of frequency ν or ν' respectively

Symbols with a bar over them denote particles with a large kinetic energy.

2.3 Matter and energy balances

Atoms and molecules are complex structures and it is only possible to investigate their collisions with other particles completely by applying quantum mechanics.

However, many of the experimental facts can be understood simply by applying some very general, and at the same time very simple, principles. These principles are:

(a) the conservation of energy

$$\Sigma W_i + \Sigma U_i + \Sigma h\nu_i = \text{Const.}$$

$\begin{cases} W_i = \text{kinetic energy} \\ U_i = \text{internal energy (see Chapter 1)} \\ \nu_i = \text{frequency of photon } i \end{cases}$

where i denotes one of the particles taking part in the reaction and not the elementary particles of which they are composed;

(b) the conservation of momentum

$$\Sigma m_i \mathbf{v}_i = \text{Const.};$$

(c) the conservation of angular momentum

$$\Sigma m_i \mathbf{r}_i \wedge \mathbf{v}_i + \sum_i \hbar \mathbf{J} = \text{Const.}$$

(the second term on the left-hand side corresponds to the rotation of the particles themselves);

(d) the conservation of charge;

(e) the conservation of mass.

These equations are as valid in the laboratory frame of reference and in a C.G. (center of gravity) frame of reference for particles in a reaction since the energy, momentum and angular momentum of the C.G. of an isolated system are the same.

In a C.G. frame of reference, the total momentum is obviously zero.

The velocities are usually small enough for it to be unnecessary to introduce a relativistic correction.

2.4 Effective cross-sections and collision frequencies

Having defined the various types of reactions which can take place in an assembly of particles, it is necessary to know their frequency. Since there are a large number of particles in a gas and the characteristics of their paths cannot be determined, this frequency cannot be calculated or measured at any given instant, and in any case it is essentially a fluctuating quantity. However, precisely because of the very large number of molecules present, it can be assumed that when the system is in equilibrium, they are uniformly distributed in space, and their velocities are distributed according to the Maxwell-Boltzmann law. Under these conditions, the fluctuations in the frequency of collisions about a mean value are very small. When a test particle is injected into the gas with a velocity v, the probability of a collision of a given type occurring is

$$d\varpi = n\sigma(v) \cdot dx \qquad (2.1)$$

where

n = number of particles per unit volume of gas

dx = distance travelled in the gas

$\sigma(v)$ = a coefficient of proportionality dependent on v and the nature of the reaction (of dimensions $[L]^2$)

= effective cross section of the collision, or, in general, of the reaction

In other words, on the basis of probability theory, if a beam of N test particles is introduced into the gas in question or if the same test particle is introduced N times (the target particles being redistributed randomly each time) which amounts to the same thing, N being large, then the number of collisions in a distance dx will be approximately

$$dN = Nd\varpi = nN\sigma(v) \, dx$$

and the larger N becomes, the more exactly will this be true.

The effective cross section has a physical meaning which is obvious in the case of collisions between particles of well-defined shape which have no influence at a distance: this is almost the case with neutral molecules, the geometric shape of which is approximately a sphere and the electric field of which decreases very rapidly with distance from the center.

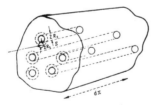

Fig. 2.1

Under these conditions, referring once more to the test particle which is assumed to be a sphere of radius R_1, it is obvious (see Fig. 2.1) that the probability of a collision with gas molecules of radius R_2 after travelling a distance dx is

$$d\varpi = \frac{s}{S} = \pi \frac{(R_1 + R_2)^2 \, n dx}{\text{unit area}} \quad \text{dimensions: [1]}$$

$d\varpi$ being a dimensionless quantity.

Substituting this in the previous definition,

$$\sigma(v) = \pi(R_1 + R_2)^2$$

it can be seen that, if $R_1 = R_2$,

$$\sigma(v) = 4\pi R_2^2$$

and if $R_1 = 0$, $\sigma(v) = \pi R_2^2 = 1/4$ of the above value (cf. molecule-molecule or molecule-electron collision).

This expression for σ should, of course, be modified to take account of the agitation of the molecules in the gas as well as the velocity v of the test particle; however, this correction is of little importance for a Maxwell-Boltzmann velocity distribution ($\sim 30\%$).

In any case, σ does not depend on the initial direction of motion of the test particle; the result is that the probability of its undergoing a collision remains constant the whole time it is among the gas molecules. Consequently, if the mean velocity of this test particle is constant, the probable number of collisions in time dt is

$$n\sigma(v)\,dx = n\sigma(v)\,v\,dt$$

The collisional frequency or the probability of collision per unit time is therefore

$$\boxed{\theta = nv\sigma(v)} \tag{2.2}$$

provided dt is large.

This equation is only strictly valid if σ is not dependent on v.

2.5 Mean free path (m.f.p.)

Finally, it is of interest to investigate the path length traversed by the test particle between collisions.

The following oversimplified reasoning can be applied. In a time τ, the particle covers in all a distance $v\tau$ and, during the same time, it undergoes in all $\theta\tau$ collisions; therefore the distance travelled between two successive collisions is given by:

$$\boxed{\lambda = \frac{v\tau}{\theta\tau} = \frac{v}{\theta} = \frac{1}{n\sigma(v)}} \tag{2.3}$$

Using a simple probability calculation, it is possible to find how far real free paths deviate from this. If a particle is to undergo its first collision between x and $x + dx$, then:

1. it must reach x without undergoing a collision,
2. it must undergo a collision between x and $x + dx$.

The probability of these two events occurring together is equal to the product of the probabilities of each occurring separately, that is:

$$(1 - n\sigma\,\mathrm{d}x)^{x/\mathrm{d}x} \cdot n\sigma\,\mathrm{d}x = \mathrm{e}^{-n\sigma x} \cdot n\sigma\,\mathrm{d}x$$

This is the probability $p(x) \cdot \mathrm{d}x$ of a free path between x and $x + \mathrm{d}x$.

Thus, by the mathematical definition of the mean, the mean free path is

$$\lambda = \int_0^\infty x \cdot p(x)\,\mathrm{d}x = \frac{1}{n\sigma}$$

as above.

It can equally be seen that the probability of a free path exceeding l (that is to say of the particle reaching at least as far as l without undergoing a collision) is

$$\varphi(l) = \mathrm{e}^{-n\sigma l} = \mathrm{e}^{-l/\lambda}$$

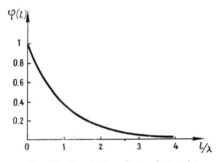

Fig. 2.2. Distribution of mean free paths

The same result can be obtained by considering a beam of particles introduced into the gas with the same velocity. Let $N(x)$ be the number of particles reaching x without undergoing a collision. The number of particles which will undergo a collision between x and $x + \mathrm{d}x$ and which must be removed from the beam will be $\mathrm{d}N = N(x) \cdot n\sigma\,\mathrm{d}x$.

Hence

$$\boxed{N(x) = N_0\,\mathrm{e}^{-n\sigma x} = N_0\varphi(x)} \qquad (2.4)$$

All the calculations above are valid either for one of the molecules of the gas under consideration or for a monoenergetic beam of particles of the same gas.

It is important to note that, if σ is independent of v, that is to say of the temperature of the gas, then

1. $\lambda \propto 1/n$: λ independent of T;
2. $\theta \propto n$ for T = Const., $\theta \propto nv \propto n\,T^{1/2}$.

This is true for a gas of neutral molecules (σ proportional to the area of the cross section of the molecules); with charged particles, σ depends to a large extent on v.

2.6 Resultant cross-sections and mean free paths

Since a collision between two identical molecules of the same gas can give rise to several different reactions (ionization, attachment, excitation. . .), the probability that any particular one of these reactions will take place is equal to the sum of the probabilities of each of these reactions (principle of total probabilities); in other words,

$$\sigma = \sigma_1 + \sigma_2 + \cdots$$

σ then being called the *resultant* or *effective cross-section*.
The probability of a particular reaction i occurring is then:

$$p_i = \sigma_i/\sigma$$

The yield of a reaction is then defined as the number of such reactions per unit length of path for a test particle:

$$Q_i = n\sigma_i \times 1 = p_i \times (1/\lambda) = 1/\lambda_i \text{ (dimensions: } [L]^{-1})$$

This is also the effective cross section per unit volume at a given pressure, usually 1 mm Hg.
Clearly

$$Q = \sum Q_i$$

If the gas is considered to be a mixture of particles with densities n_1, $n_2 \ldots n_j$, the total effective cross section for a test particle of type k and velocity v is given by

$$\sigma_k = \frac{1}{n} \sum_j n_j \sigma_{jk}$$

the frequency of collisions,

$$\theta_k = v_k \sum_j n_j \sigma_{jk}$$

and the mean free path,

$$\lambda_k = \frac{1}{\sum_j n_j \sigma_{jk}}.$$

2.7 Orders of magnitude of cross-sections and mean free paths

The reaction between two atomic or molecular particles in a neutral or ionized gas chiefly involves only the surfaces of the particles which take part, that is the outer shells of their electron clouds. A test molecule has only to approach within a few molecular radii of the target molecule for a collision to occur, giving rise to one of the reactions mentioned above. It is therefore not surprising to find that the majority of effective cross-sections investigated are of the order of magnitude of the geometrical cross-section of the molecules, that is to say

$$\sim 10 \cdot (10^{-8})^2 = 10^{-15} \, \text{cm}^2$$

The density of the molecules in a gas at $0 \,°C$ and $760 \, mm \, Hg$ is: $n \approx 2.7 \times 10^{19} \, cm^{-3}$ (Loschmidt's number). Hence:

$$\lambda = 1/n\sigma = 1/Q \approx 10^{-5} \, \text{cm}$$

These quantities depend to a large extent, of course, on the relative velocity of the particles in question. In fact it is this which determines the energy available; if it is not sufficient, the reaction may not take place. If, on the other hand, the velocity is too great, the time for which the forces act is short, and the probability of the reaction occurring is again reduced. The numerical values given above only indicate a rough order of magnitude. However, they do at least justify using the area of the first orbit of the Bohr hydrogen atom as the unit of effective cross-section, that is:

$$\pi a_0^2 = 8.8 \cdot 10^{-17} \, \text{cm}^2 \approx 10^{-16} \, \text{cm}^2$$

Note: Nuclear reactions involve particles with much smaller dimensions: the nuclear radius is of the order of 10^{-12} cm; the effective cross-sections are of the order 10^{-24} cm^2, and the unit used is the *barn* which is 10^{-24} cm^2.

REFERENCES

Kinetic Theory of Gases

KENNARD, *Kinetic Theory of Gases* (McGraw-Hill, U.S.A., 1938).
CHAPMAN and COWLING, *Mathematical Theory of Non-uniform Gases* (Cambridge, G.B., 1958).

Collision Theory

MOTT and MASSEY, *Theory of Atomic Collisions* (OUP, 1949) (Quantum Theory of Collisions).
CHAPMAN and COWLING, and classical works on mechanics.

Numerical and Experimental Data

MASSEY and BURHOP, *Electronic and Ionic Impact Phenomena* (Clarendon Press, Oxford, 1952).
FLUGGE, Editor,*Handbuch der Physik*, XXI (Springer 1956).
LOEB, *Fundamental Processes of Electrical Discharges in Gases* (J. Wiley, U.S.A., 1939); *Basic Processes of Gaseous Electronics* (University Press, 1955).
VON ENGEL,*Ionized Gases* (Clarendon Press, G.B., 1956).
BROWN, *Basic Data of Plasma Physics* (MIT, U.S.A., 1960).
ALLISON, *Review of Modern Physics*, 30, 1137 (1957).

General Articles on Plasmas and Gas Discharges

THOMSON and THOMSON, *Conduction of Electricity Through Gases*, I and II (Cambridge, U.P., 1936).
PENNING, *Electric Discharges in Gases* (Dunod, 1958).
FRANCIS, *Ionization Phenomena in Gases* (Butterworth, 1960) (contains numerous recent references).
FLUGGE, Editor,*Handbuch der Physik*, XXII (Springer, 1956).
DELCROIX, *Theory of Ionized Gases* (Dunod, 1959).
COBINE, *Gaseous Conductors* (McGraw-Hill, U.S.A., 1941).
K. K. DARROW,*Electrical Phenomena in Gases* (Williams, U.S.A., 1932).
J. S. TOWNSEND, *Electricity in Gases.*
LAPORTE, *Electrical Discharges in Gases*   (A. Colin, Fr., 1948).
BAYET, *Electron Physics of Gases and Solids* (Masson, Fr., 1958).
HASTED, *Physics of Atomic Collisions* (Butterworth, G. B., 1964).
McDANIEL, *Collision phenomena in ionized gases*, Wiley, U. S. A., 1964.
BARNETT, *Atomic and molecular collision cross sections*, ORNL 3113, U. S. A., 1964.

3   elastic collisions

3.1 Definition

Elastic collisions between two particles of matter are collisions which leave the total kinetic energy of the system, and consequently the internal energy, unchanged.

These collisions are practically the only kind which occur in neutral gases, and in a gas which is highly ionized they still make up a large part of the total number of collisions.

In neutral gases it is elastic collisions which allow thermodynamic equilibrium to be established. In ionized gases, they usually contribute to the establishment, if not of thermodynamic equilibrium, then at least of a steady state.

3.2 Basic theory of elastic collisions

The first approximation that is made (neglecting quantum and relativistic theory) is to assume that we are dealing with particles of constant mass, with spherical symmetry and a velocity which is small compared with the velocity of light. The laws of classical mechanics can then be applied.

3.2.1 Trajectory

Let $f(r)$ be the force acting between two particles separated by a distance r [$f(r)$ is assumed to tend to zero when r tends to infinity]; let $\mathbf{r}_1$ and $\mathbf{r}_2$ be the position vectors of the two particles where

$$\mathbf{r} = \mathbf{r}_1 - \mathbf{r}_2 = r\mathbf{r}_0$$

C

r_0 being a unit vector (see Fig. 3.1). Then:

$$m_1 \ddot{r}_1 = - m_2 \ddot{r}_2 = f(r)\, r_0$$

Hence

$$\ddot{r} = \ddot{r}_1 - \ddot{r}_2 = \left(\frac{m_1 + m_2}{m_1 m_2} \right) f(r)\, r_0$$

Now this is the equation of motion of a particle M of mass

$$\mu = \frac{m_1 m_2}{m_1 + m_2}$$

gravitating about a center of force O' with a position vector $O'M = r$, the force function being $f(r)$. In other words, when investigating the relative motion of the two particles, one of them can be considered to be stationary provided that the other is regarded as having a reduced mass μ. The trajectory described will be entirely in the plane containing the center of force, that is, the stationary particle.

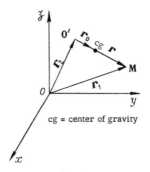

cg = center of gravity

Fig. 3.1

In the reduced mass system of coordinates, the theorem for the kinetic energy can be written:

$$d(\tfrac{1}{2}\, \mu v^2) = f(r)\, dr = - dU(r)$$

where
$v = |\dot{r}| =$ relative velocity of the two particles,
$U(r) =$ potential function from which the central force $f(r)$ is derived; assumed to tend to zero as $r \to \infty$.

Hence,

$$\tfrac{1}{2}\, \mu v^2 + U = \text{Const.}$$

$U = 0$ a long time before and a long time after the collision. If the indices a (ante) and p (post) respectively denote quantities corresponding to states a long time before and a long time after the collision, then

$$v_a = v_p$$

Only the direction of the relative velocity is altered in an elastic collision.

To find the change in direction, let us consider the plane in which the imaginary particle with reduced mass is moving (see Fig. 3.2). The trajectory will, in general, be of the type shown, the center O being on the convex or concave side of the curve depending on whether the potential $\varphi(r)$ is repulsive or attractive.

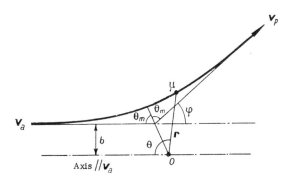

Fig. 3.2. $v_p = v_a$; b = "impact parameter;" $\varphi = \pi - 2\theta_m$: deflection

The equation for the conservation of angular momentum about O can be written

$$\mu v_a b = \mu r^2 \dot{\theta} \tag{3.1}$$

The equation for the conservation of energy in the reduced mass system of coordinates will be:

$$\tfrac{1}{2}\mu v_a^2 = \tfrac{1}{2}\mu(\dot{r}^2 + r^2\dot{\theta}^2) + U(r) \tag{3.2}$$

Eliminating $\dot{\theta}$ between these two equations,

$$\tfrac{1}{2}\mu v_a^2 = \tfrac{1}{2}\mu\dot{r}^2 + \tfrac{1}{2}\mu v_a^2 b^2/r^2 + U(r)$$

or

$$\frac{dr}{dt} = \pm\, v_a \sqrt{1 - \frac{b^2}{r^2} - \frac{U(r)}{\frac{1}{2}\,\mu v_a^2}} \tag{3.3}$$

Equation (3.1) can also be written

$$d\theta/dt = bv_a/r^2 \tag{3.4}$$

Combining (3.3) and (3.4)

$$\frac{dr}{d\theta} = \pm\, \frac{r^2}{b} \sqrt{1 - \frac{b^2}{r^2} - \frac{U(r)}{\frac{1}{2}\,\mu v_a^2}} \tag{3.5}$$

If the root vanishes at a value for r of r_m, then r_m is the shortest distance between the two particles. Associated with the position vector r_m is a polar angle θ_m, the direction of r_m being an axis of symmetry of the trajectory, the two signs in (3.5) giving the two halves of this trajectory.

Finally, on integrating (3.5)

$$\theta_m = \int_{r_m}^{\infty} \frac{b\, dr/r^2}{\sqrt{1 - \frac{b^2}{r^2} - \frac{U(r)}{\frac{1}{2}\,\mu v_a^2}}}$$

and

$$\varphi(b, v_a) = \pi - 2\int_{r_m}^{\infty} \frac{b\, dr/r^2}{\sqrt{1 - \frac{b^2}{r^2} - \frac{U(r)}{\frac{1}{2}\,\mu v_a^2}}} \tag{3.6}$$

In the particular (ideal) case of a collision between two perfectly elastic spheres with $U(r) = 0$, the trajectory is made up of two straight lines symmetric with respect to θ_m (the two asymptotes in Fig. 3.2). $dr/d\theta$ does not vanish but changes sign instantaneously at $r = r_m$. r_m and θ_m then define the positions of the two particles in relation to the center during the infinitely short time they are in contact. The directions of v_a and v_p are symmetrical with respect to the line joining the centers at the moment of collision.

In this case, if r_1 and r_2 are the radii of the two spheres involved, then

$$r_m = r_1 + r_2\,; \qquad \theta_m = \arcsin\frac{b}{r_1 + r_2}\,;$$
$$\varphi = \pi - 2\,\theta_m \tag{3.7}$$

3.2.2 Effective cross-section of elastic collision

Having defined the various possible trajectories during the collision process, let us now calculate the probability of collision or effective cross section for these trajectories.

Let a beam of N test particles with velocity v be introduced into a gas of density n. As a result of elastic collisions, the test particles will be deflected and distributed in all directions about the initial direction (see Fig. 3.3).

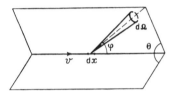

Fig. 3.3

The number of particles deflected into an element of solid angle $d\Omega$, with its center on the axis (θ, φ), as a result of collisions undergone in the interval dx will be

$$dN = \sigma(\theta, \varphi)\, Nn\, d\Omega\, dx$$

where σ is a constant of proportionality with the dimensions of an area called the differential effective cross section for an elastic collision (cf. Section 2.4); we shall now determine this. Since it was assumed that the particles have spherical symmetry, we can presume that the deflected test particles will be distributed uniformly about the v axis: σ is then only a function of φ. The probability of scattering in the space defined by two cones with semiangles of φ and $\varphi + d\varphi$ will then be

$$p(\varphi)\, d\varphi = \frac{dN}{N} = \int_{\varphi}^{\varphi+d\varphi} n\sigma(\varphi)\, dx\, d\Omega \tag{3.8}$$
$$= 2\pi n\sigma(\varphi) \sin \varphi\, d\varphi\, dx$$

On the other hand, if φ is to be in the interval $d\varphi$, b must be between b and $b + db$, the relation between b and φ being that given in (3.6). But, considering a test particle, the probability of its distance from a target particle being in the interval b to $b + db$ is equal to the mean number of target particles between two cylinders of radius b and $b + db$, length dx and with their axes on the trajectory of the test particle. This number is clearly

$$\rho(b) \cdot db = \frac{dN}{1} = n \cdot 2\,\pi b \cdot db \cdot dx \tag{3.9}$$

It can also be stated that, as in Section 2.4, each target particle should be assigned an effective cross section $2\pi b\,db$; the desired probability is therefore

$$\frac{s}{S} = \frac{(nS\,dx)\,2\pi b \cdot db}{S} = 2\pi n b \cdot db \cdot dx$$

Comparing (3.8) and (3.9), we find:

$$\sigma(\varphi, v_a) = \frac{b}{\sin\varphi}\left|\frac{db}{d\varphi}\right| \qquad (3.10)$$

The total effective cross section, which defines the probability that a test particle will be deflected by a given angle in an interval dx, is clearly

$$\sigma_{el} = \int_{\varphi=0}^{\pi} \sigma(\varphi, v_a)\,d\Omega = 2\pi \int_0^\pi \sigma(\varphi, v_a)\sin\varphi\,d\varphi$$

Particular cases:

1. Impenetrable particles with $U(r) = 0$ ("billiard ball" type). From (3.7)

$$db = (r_1 + r_2)\cos\theta_m,$$
$$b \cdot db = (r_1 + r_2)^2 \sin\theta_m \cos\theta_m\,d\theta_m$$
$$= -\tfrac{1}{4}(r_1 + r_2)^2 \sin\varphi\,d\varphi$$

Finally

$$\sigma = \tfrac{1}{4}(r_1 + r_2)^2 \qquad (3.11)$$

which is independent of φ and v_a; the scattering is isotropic in the center of gravity system and in the reduced mass system (cf. Section 3.2.1).

Under these conditions, the total effective cross section for elastic collisions is

$$\sigma_{el} = 4\pi\sigma = \pi(r_1 + r_2)^2$$

2. Coulomb collisions. In this case the interaction potential is of the form

$$U(r) = q_1 q_2 / r$$

where q_1 and q_2 are the electric charges of the two particles.

The trajectory of each of the two particles in a center of gravity system is a hyperbola, as is the trajectory of the imaginary particle in the reduced mass system.

We find that

$$\sigma(\varphi, v_a) = \frac{1}{4} \left(\frac{q_1 q_2}{\mu v_a^2} \right)^2 \frac{1}{\sin^4 \varphi/2} \qquad (3.12)$$

This is Rutherford's very important formula. It can be seen that σ tends to ∞ very rapidly when $\varphi \to 0$; net scattering is in a forward direction ("persistence of direction").

Under these conditions, the total effective collision cross section no longer has any meaning, since it is not finite because of the lower limit $\varphi = 0$. This was to be expected because, whatever the distance of a charged test particle from an equally charged target particle, there will always be a force between them which will deflect them, by however small an amount, from their original trajectories.

The concept of total effective collision cross section is therefore not well suited to experimental investigation. Besides, even the differential effective cross sections calculated from the theory given above do not entirely conform to reality. In fact, experiment shows that the effective cross sections for collisions between electrons or ions on the one hand, and molecules on the other hand, are independent neither of the scattering direction nor of the energy of the particles, which contradicts the above results for "billiard ball" particles. Furthermore, in the case of charged particles, the Rutherford formula is clearly false for $\varphi \approx 0$. A more elaborate theory is therefore required.

3.2.3 Transfer of momentum

The phenomena of diffusion, viscosity and heat conduction in gases are based on the exchange of momentum or energy between particles by collision; that is why they are called transport or transfer phenomena.

If, in a collision, a particle undergoes a deflection φ, the change in its momentum in the initial direction is

$$\Delta(mv) = mv(\cos \varphi - 1)$$

By definition, the mean value of the relative change $\Delta(mv)/mv$ is:

$$\left\langle \frac{\Delta(mv)}{mv} \right\rangle = \int_0^\pi (\cos \cdot \varphi - 1) \, p(\varphi) \, d\varphi$$

$$= 2\pi n \, dx \int_0^\pi \sigma(\varphi) \sin \varphi \, (\cos \varphi - 1) \, d\varphi$$

By analogy with the formula for an effective cross section $dN/N = -n \sigma \, dx$ [cf. Eq. (2.4)], we can define an effective cross section, σ_m, for diffusion or transfer of momentum by

$$\sigma_m = 2\pi \int_0^\pi \sigma(\varphi) \, (1 - \cos \varphi) \sin \varphi \, d\varphi \qquad (3.13)$$

such that

$$\left\langle \frac{(\Delta mv)}{mv} \right\rangle = -n \sigma_m \, dx$$

Note that, if the diffusion is isotropic ($\sigma(\varphi)$ = Const.),

$$\sigma_m = \int_0^\pi \sigma \cdot 2\pi \sin \varphi \cdot d\varphi = \int_0^\pi \sigma \, d\Omega = 4\pi\sigma$$

σ_m = total effective cross section for elastic collision = σ_{el}.

The corresponding mean free paths $\lambda_m = 1/n\sigma_m$ and $\lambda_{el} = 1/n\sigma_{el}$ will therefore be the same. Now, after traversing a path length λ_m, the relative change in momentum (in the initial direction) is $n\sigma_m \lambda_m = -1$. In other words, after each elastic collision, the velocity vector of a particle is, on the average, turned through an angle of $\pi/2$.

If $\sigma(\varphi) \neq$ constant, this is no longer true; the number of elastic collisions needed to deflect a particle by $\pi/2$ is $\sigma_{el}/\sigma_m > 1$ or < 1 depending on whether the particles are mostly scattered forwards (persistence of direction) or mostly backwards.

3.2.4 Energy transfer

Let us now attempt to determine the quantity of energy transferred between two particles at the time of a collision. Let us therefore consider the system of coordinates having its origin at the C.G. of the two particles. This frame of reference is displaced parallel to itself with the velocity $\mathbf{v}_g$ of the C.G.; this velocity is constant in the laboratory system if no exterior forces act on the two particles. With the notation in Fig. 3.1,

$$\mathbf{r}_1 = \frac{m_2}{m_1 + m_2} \, \mathbf{r}, \qquad \mathbf{r}_2 = -\left(\frac{m_1}{m_1 + m_2}\right) \mathbf{r}$$

and

$$\mathbf{v}_1 = \frac{m_2 \mathbf{v}}{m_1 + m_2}, \qquad \mathbf{v}_2 = -\left(\frac{m_1}{m_1 + m_2}\right) \mathbf{v}$$

When the two particles are still a long distance apart, their relative velocities are both more or less directed towards the C.G. (Fig. 3.4) (if not they would never meet).

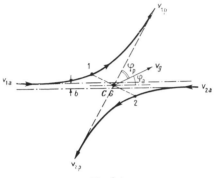

Fig. 3.4

This is still true a long time after the collision, but the relative velocities then make an angle φ with the initial velocities without their absolute magnitudes being altered (since $v_a = v_p$).

According to the theory of vector addition the velocities V_1 and V_2 of particles m_1 and m_2 are given in the laboratory system of coordinates a long time prior to and a long time after the collision by

$$V_{1a}^2 = v_g^2 + v_{1a}^2 + 2\,v_{1a}v_g \cos \varphi_a$$
$$V_{1p}^2 = v_g^2 + v_{1p}^2 + 2\,v_{1p}v_g \cos \varphi_p$$
$$V_{2a}^2 = v_g^2 + v_{2a}^2 - 2\,v_{2a}v_g \cos \varphi_a$$
$$V_{2p}^2 = v_g^2 + v_{2p}^2 - 2\,v_{2p}v_g \cos \varphi_p$$

Here the symbols v and V represent the absolute values and the directions of the velocities are defined by the angles φ_a and φ_p.

Since

$$v_{1a} = v_{1p} = \frac{m_2}{m_1 + m_2}\,v_a \quad \text{and} \quad v_{2a} = v_{2p} = \frac{m_1 v_a}{m_1 + m_2}$$

the amount of energy acquired by m_1 is

$$\varepsilon = \frac{\frac{1}{2}\,m_1 \big(V_{1p}^2 - V_{1a}^2\big)}{\frac{1}{2}\,m_1 V_{1a}^2 + \frac{1}{2}\,m_2 V_{2a}^2} = -\frac{\frac{1}{2}\,m_1^2 \big(V_{2p}^2 - V_{2a}^2\big)}{\frac{1}{2}\,m_1 V_{1a}^2 + \frac{1}{2}\,m_2 V_{2a}^2}$$
$$= \frac{2\,m_1 m_2}{(m_1 + m_2)^2} \cdot \frac{v_a v_g (\cos \varphi_p - \cos \varphi_a)}{v_g^2 + v_a^2 (m_1 m_2 / M^2)}$$

Note that, when the C.G. is stationary $(v_g = 0)$, $\varepsilon = 0$ and that, all other things being equal, ε is a maximum for

$$v_g = \frac{\sqrt{m_1 m_2}}{m_1 + m_2} \, v_a$$

when

$$\varepsilon = \frac{\sqrt{m_1 m_2}}{m_1 + m_2} \, (\cos \varphi_a - \cos \varphi_p)$$

In the most usual case where one of the particles (atoms) is very heavy and practically at rest $(m_1 \to \infty, V_1 \to 0,\ V_2 = v_a,\ v_g = m_2 v_a/(m_1 + m_2),\ \varphi_a = -\pi)$, while the other particle (electron) is light and fast, it can be seen that

$$\boxed{\varepsilon \approx \frac{2\,m_2}{m_1} \, (1 + \cos \varphi_p)} \tag{3.14}$$

So that $0 < \varepsilon \ll 1$.

The energy transfer is then of little importance and is always accomplished at the expense of the light particle.

Conversely, if the two particles in question have similar masses (gas ions), the energy transfer may reach $\varepsilon = 1$; on average, if the scattering (diffusion) is isotropic, $\varepsilon \approx \frac{1}{2}$ since $(1 + \cos \varphi_p) \approx 1$.

Thus energy is transferred much more readily between particles of the same type than between particles with widely different masses. Since it is in fact these transfers which allow thermo-dynamic equilibrium to be set up, it can be concluded that, in a gas, the various types of particles will, in general, have different energies even in equilibrium.

Thus, in an electric discharge, the electrons accelerated by the electric field are losing very little energy (at least due to elastic collisions) and will, on average, have a higher temperature (that is to say energy) than the ions which are very slow. In effect, if $\mathcal{C}$ is the work done by an electric field E on a particle of charge e, mass m and velocity v, initially equal to v_0, then

$$\tfrac{1}{2}\,mv^2 - \tfrac{1}{2}\,mv_0^2 = \mathcal{C} \;; \qquad d\mathcal{C}/dt = eEv$$

Whence

$$\frac{d(\mathcal{C} + \tfrac{1}{2}\,mv_0^2)}{\sqrt{\mathcal{C} + \tfrac{1}{2}\,mv_0^2}} = 2\,d(\sqrt{\mathcal{C} + \tfrac{1}{2}\,mv_0^2}) = \sqrt{2/m}\ eE\ dt$$

and

$$\mathcal{C} = \frac{(eE)^2}{2m}\,t^2 + eEv_0 t$$

Thus in the same interval of time (long enough for the second term to be negligible if $v_0 \neq 0$), a proton will gain 1836 times less kinetic energy than an electron in the same electric field.

Examples: ions and molecules at 0.04 eV (ambient temperature), electrons at several eV (some 10^4 °K).

3.3 Theory of collisions from the viewpoint of wave mechanics

According to Heisenberg's uncertainty principle, it is impossible to know precisely the position and the velocity of the same particle simultaneously. The concept of a trajectory loses all meaning. It is replaced by the concept of a wave analogous to that in optics. At every point in space, a function $\psi(r, t)$ is defined the square of the modulus of which, that is $|\psi|^2$, represents the density probability (i.e., the fraction of total number of particles) or the probability per unit volume of finding one of the particles of the assembly at a point r at time t. Thus a cylindrical beam of mono-energetic particles with velocity v parallel to Oz is considered to be a plane wave represented by the function:

$$\psi_1 = A \exp[i(Et/\hbar - kz)]$$

where
E = kinetic energy of each particle
$\hbar = h/2\pi$; h = Planck's constant
k = propagation constant = $2\pi/\lambda$
λ = de Broglie wavelength = h/mv
m = mass of each particle

The wave intensity is $|\psi_1|^2 = A^2$.

Now the target particle represents an obstacle in the path of this wave. As in optics, it will give rise to a diffracted spherical wave

$$\psi_2 = A \frac{f(\varphi)}{r} \exp[i(Et/\hbar - \mathbf{k} \cdot \mathbf{r})]$$

The function $f(\varphi)$ represents in this case the scattering properties of the obstacle, both as to intensity and as to angular distribution. The factor r in the denominator represents the weakening of the diffracted wave with distance from the center of scattering. The obstacle is taken as the origin of the coordinate system.

The resultant wave, $\psi_1 + \psi_2$, is, like all functions in wave mechanics, a solution to a particular Schrödinger equation, analogous to the equation for the propagation of electromagnetic waves. The equation can be solved to give $\psi_2(r, t)$ as a function of $\psi_1(r, t)$. Since $|\psi_2(r)|^2$ represents the density probability of finding a particle at point **r**, it can be seen that the effective cross section for elastic diffusion is connected with it (in accordance with the definition of σ) by the relation

$$(vA^2) \cdot \sigma(\varphi, v_a) \cdot d\Omega = |\psi_2|^2 \cdot v \cdot (r^2 \, d\Omega)$$

or

$$\sigma(\varphi, v_a) = (f(\varphi))^2$$

In Fig. 3.5 comparison can be made between the broad outlines of the results from the "billiard ball," Rutherford and wave mechanical theories for the differential effective cross section for elastic collisions between electrons and neutral molecules with given energies.

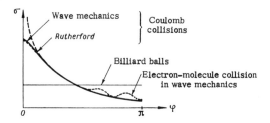

Fig. 3.5. The various theories for the differential effective cross section for elastic collisions

In general, experiment agrees with the wave theory at least within the limits of resolution of the measuring apparatus. It is not possible, in fact, to reduce indefinitely the aperture of the collimator slits which define the direction of diffraction φ. A limit is imposed not only by the sensitivity of the detectors but also by the nature of quantum mechanics itself. Let us suppose that we wish to measure the differential effective cross section associated with an impact parameter y and a corresponding angle of deviation φ (Fig. 3.6).

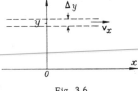

Fig. 3.6

To define the trajectory in the classical manner, the uncertainty in y and in the orientation of the velocity of the test particle must be small, that is:

$$\frac{\Delta y}{y} \ll 1 \quad \text{and} \quad \frac{\Delta v_y}{v_x} \ll \varphi$$

But, according to Heisenberg's uncertainty principle:

$$\Delta y \cdot \Delta v_y \approx h/m$$

or

$$y\varphi \gg h/mv_x$$

Now $y\varphi \to 0$ when $\varphi \to 0$; thus the uncertainty principle imposes a lower limit on φ and an upper limit on y. Under these conditions, the total effective cross section ceases to be infinite and the paradox of classical mechanics is resolved.

3.4 Experimental results

In conclusion, we shall describe some experimental results and comment upon them. These results relate to collisions between electrons and molecules (or atoms), ions and molecules, and molecules and molecules.

In the most usual gas discharges, the density of charged particles (electrons and ions) is low and the frequency of collisions with each other is much lower than that of their collisions with neutral molecules.

All we need to know about them is that their total effective cross sections are proportional to the square of the product of the electrical charges and inversely proportional to the square of the energy of the incident particle, as in Rutherford's formula (Eq. 3.12).

3.4.1 Electron-molecule collisions

3.4.1.1 Angular distribution. Figure 3.7 represents the effective differential cross section as a function of the scattering angle for different energies of the incident electron.

The general character of the curve is reminiscent of that for diffraction by a small screen or a grating. This phenomenon can be understood well on the basis of wave mechanics. If the incident beam is considered as a plane wave, the effects of diffraction will be felt when the wavelength

$$\lambda = h/mv = \sqrt{154/V} \cdot 10^{-8} \text{cm}$$

is of the same order of magnitude as the "radius" (in the sense of center of force) of the atom or molecule, that is to say, if I' is between ≈ 1 and tens of eV.

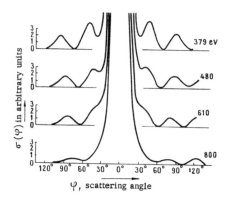

Fig. 3.7. $\sigma(\varphi)$ for electron-molecule collisions with different values for the kinetic energy of the electrons (in eV) (G. FRANCIS, *Ionization Phenomena in Gases*, Butterworth, 1960, p. 17)

For higher energies, the wavelength is small in comparison with the dimensions of the target which tends to give a well-defined shadow; only very small angles of diffraction occur.

Finally, for energies less than 1 eV, the de Broglie wavelength is much larger than the target. It is assumed that scattering is then isotropic and independent of the energy (σ independent of φ and v_a, law of neutral "billiard ball" type).

3.4.1.2 Total effective cross section. Figures 3.8, 3.9 and 3.10 represent these cross sections for helium and hydrogen, alkaline metal vapors and rare gases respectively.

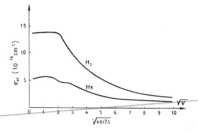

Fig. 3.8

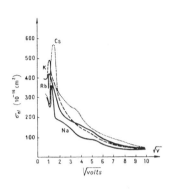

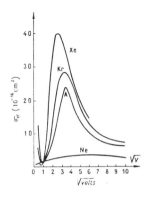

Fig. 3.9   Fig. 3.10

It should be noted that, far from obeying the "billiard ball theory," σ_{el} varies a great deal with incident energy except in the case of He and H_2 at very low energies.

Nevertheless, atoms from the same column in the periodic table behave, on the whole, in the same manner. Thus the curves are very similar for the alkaline metals on the one hand, and for the rare gases on the other.

However, the effective cross-section of the alkaline metals is a great deal higher than for rare gases (because their electron clouds are more diffuse).

It can also be seen that the *Ramsauer resonance effect** is very marked for rare gases. The effective cross-section falls to a very low value at a certain energy of the order of 1 eV; this too is a diffraction effect; the phases of the de Broglie waves diffracted by different points in the atom are such that the resultant intensity of the diffracted wave is everywhere very small; the target is thus almost transparent to a beam of electrons. By a similar mechanism maxima may occur in the effective cross-section/accelerating potential diagram.

In every case the effective cross-sections decrease regularly as the energy increases beyond $\approx$ 20 eV. This phenomenon is of great importance in certain electric discharges since it can give rise to uncoupled electrons which, having passed the peak at 20 eV, lose less and less energy due to collisions as they progressively gain energy from the electric field.

---

*Editor's Footnote: i.e., the fact that the cross-section reaches a maximum value for a particular accelerating potential and decreases for low energies.

3.4.2 Ion-molecule collisions

Figures 3.11 and 3.12 show that the total effective cross sections for elastic ion-molecule collisions decrease slowly and uniformly with energy when the latter is not very high (less than a few hundred eV).

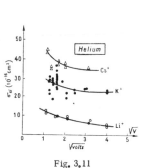

Fig. 3.11

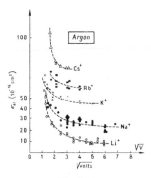

Fig. 3.12

In this case, in fact, the de Broglie wavelength h/Mv of the incident ions is much smaller than the dimensions of the target and there are no diffraction effects: the classical theory can thus be applied. The effective cross sections therefore vary very little and are of the order of magnitude of the area of the geometrical cross section of the atoms. Moreover these two quantities increase with atomic number for target atoms belonging to the same family in the periodic table. As in the case of electron-molecule collisions, they are higher in the case of alkaline metals than in the case of the rare gases.

At higher energies, it is no longer possible to distinguish elastic collisions from inelastic collisions easily.

3.4.3 Molecule-molecule collisions

These collisions govern the behavior of neutral gases. They are extremely difficult to investigate experimentally because of difficulties of detection. Nevertheless it is reasonable to think that, on the whole, they obey the "billiard ball" laws since the van der Waals forces between molecules decrease very rapidly with distance ($\sim 1/r^7$). This hypothesis is also justified by approximate verification of the consequences it would entail in connection with the kinetic theory of gases.

As an indication, Table 3.1 gives values for the mean free path $\lambda(=1/n\sigma)$ for some common gases.

Table 3.1. Mean free paths at $0°C$ and 1 mm Hg $(n = 3.54 \cdot 10^{16}\,cm^{-3})$

	He	H_2	A	N_2	O_2
$\lambda(cm) \times 10^3$	17.6	14.2	8.1	6.7	7

Note: According to the "billiard ball" theory, we should have:

$$\sigma_{m-m} \approx \sigma_{i-m} \approx 4\sqrt{2}\,\sigma_{e-m} \tag{3.15}$$

The factor 4 arises from the hypothesis that the geometric radius of an electron is infinitely small; the factor $\sqrt{2}$ results from the fact that molecules, as well as electrons, move with an irregular velocity due to thermal agitation.

D

4 inelastic collisions (I): excitation, ionization

4.1 Definition

We have already seen in Chapter 2 that an inelastic collision is one in which the internal energy of the particles changes as well as the kinetic energy. Photons can take part in such collisions. We have also seen that the number and diversity of the possible reactions increases with the complexity of the particles involved.

Table 2.1 shows that inelastic collisions can be grouped under the titles: excitation, ionization, recombination, charge transfer, attachment and detachment, dissociation.

It can also be seen that these reactions cannot take place in a gas in which the atoms are entirely ionized and far removed from any material surface (hot stars). However, these reactions play an important, even dominant, part in most terrestrial electric discharges since the kinetic or photon energy reaches several eV ($1 \text{ eV} = 1.6 \times 10^{-12}$ erg): this is the order of magnitude of the excitation threshold of atoms.

4.2 Reaction threshold

An inelastic collision of the first kind, characterized by a variation ΔU in the internal energy, can only occur if an amount ΔU of the kinetic energy of the two particles involved can be converted into internal energy. Now there is an upper limit to the kinetic energy,

ΔW, available for such a conversion. In effect, since the energy of the C.G. must remain constant, the sum of the separate "relative" kinetic energies can be transformed into internal energy.

It can easily be seen that this sum is equal to the kinetic energy of the particle with reduced mass in the corresponding system of coordinates:

$$W = W_r = \tfrac{1}{2}\frac{m_1 m_2}{m_1 + m_2}v^2 = \frac{m_1}{m_1 + m_2}(\tfrac{1}{2}m_2 v^2) = \frac{m_2}{m_1 + m_2}(\tfrac{1}{2}m_1 v^2)$$

where v = relative velocity of the two particles.

Thus, when the two particles have widely different masses and the lighter of them is at rest, the energy available for conversion to internal energy is only a fraction ($\approx$ light mass/heavy mass) of the kinetic energy of the incident particle; the rest is attached to the center of gravity which is displaced with almost the same velocity as the heavy particle.

If the two particles have similar masses, the available kinetic energy reaches half the initial energy of the particles involved.

Diagrams showing effective cross sections (Fig. 4.1) generally have kinetic energy E (or velocity) of one particle as abscissa, the other being assumed to be initially at rest. For $E < E_s$ the threshold energy), the inelastic collision in question cannot take place. E_s is only $\approx \Delta U$ when the incident particle is a great deal lighter than the other. In general

$$E_s = \Delta U \left(\frac{m_1 + m_2}{m_2}\right)$$

if m_2 is stationary.

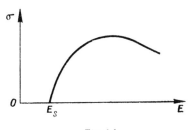

Fig. 4.1

If one of the two particles is a photon (incident at high velocity c), all its energy is available; this can be considered either as internal energy or as kinetic energy corresponding to infinitely small mass.

Then

$$E_s = \Delta U$$

Note: 1) σ is dependent only on the relative motion of the two particles. 2) If $\Delta U < 0$, the reaction has no threshold; i.e., reaction is possible whatever the value of E.

4.3 Excitation

When an atom (or molecule) has absorbed a sufficient amount of energy for one of its electrons (generally that farthest from the nucleus) to pass to a higher energy level, the atom (or molecule) is said to have been excited: its internal energy has been increased by the difference $\Delta U = eV^*$ between the energies of the final and initial states (see Chapter 1, Tables 1.2 and 1.3).

The initial energy level of the excited particle is not necessarily that corresponding to the ground state.

4.3.1 Excitation by photons

The reaction can be represented by the following general equation:

$$h\nu + A \rightarrow A^* \tag{4.1}$$

The reaction threshold is defined by

$$\boxed{h\nu = eV^*} \quad \text{or} \quad \boxed{\lambda(\text{Å}) = \frac{12,400}{V^*(\text{volts})}} \tag{4.2}$$

However, even with higher energy photons, the reaction may not take place. In fact, according to a more or less accepted principle (that of microscopic reversibility due to Klein and Rosseland), any binary action in an assembly must be in equilibrium with the inverse reaction. Now the inverse reaction to (4.1) is the emission of a photon by an atom:

$$A^* \rightarrow A + h\nu$$

and ν can only have discrete values determined by the energy levels of the atom.

Thus the effective excitation cross section has the form shown in Fig. 4.2.

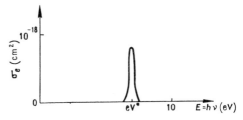

Fig. 4.2. Excitation by photons

Furthermore, $(\sigma_e)_{max}$ itself is very small: of the order of 10^{-18} cm² or less. This is due to the fact that, in accordance with the principle of conservation of momentum, a reaction of this kind can only take place if the collision is head on; otherwise the excited atom would have a transverse component of velocity after the collision not compensated by that of the photon, and in addition the probability of a direct collision taking place is very small.

Even if the condition $h\nu \geqslant eV^*$ is satisfied, the reaction is not always possible: according to the rules of selection, there are metastable levels from which an atomic electron cannot descend to a lower level by emitting a photon; similarly, a photon cannot elevate an electron to such a level. The corresponding effective cross section is thus very small.

On the other hand, excitation by a resonance line is highly probable, as is the emission of the same line. This phenomenon gives rise to a trapping of radiation, characterized by a relatively high population of the resonance level.

Moreover the atom may be excited again, before returning to the initial level, and undergo a transition to a higher level. Thus an atom can be ionized due to cumulative excitation by photons with an energy lower than the ionization energy.

4.3.2 Excitation by electrons

The basic reaction is:

$$e^- + A \to e^- + A^* \tag{4.3}$$

If the target is at rest and the incident electron has a kinetic energy E, the reaction can only occur if

$$E \geqslant eV^*$$

However, the probability of excitation remains very low close to the threshold energy E_s, since it is difficult to fulfill the condition of conservation of angular momentum. If the result of excitation is to modify the quantum number J by an amount ΔJ, the angular momentum of the incident electron must alter in the course of the collision by an amount which will exactly compensate the change $\hbar\Delta J$ in the internal angular momentum of the excited atom. But, if $E \approx eV^*$, the electron would remain at rest after the collision; thus if the reaction is to occur, the initial angular momentum of the electron must be exactly equal to $\hbar\Delta J$, which is highly improbable.

The effective excitation cross-section therefore increases rather slowly with E until it reaches a maximum, $(\sigma_e)_{max}$, which corresponds to an energy several times higher than E_s (several eV for heavy atoms; several tens of eV for light atoms). $(\sigma_e)_{max}$ is of the order of 10^{-16} cm^2 for an allowed transition, but very much smaller for a forbidden transition ($\sim 10^{-19}$ cm^2, for example).

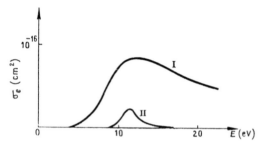

Fig. 4.3. Excitation by electrons. I—allowed transition, decreases as $(\log E)/E$; II—forbidden transition, decreases as $1/E$

After the maximum, the curve decreases with $(\log E)/E$ for an allowed transition, or more rapidly, with $1/E$, for a forbidden transition.

Finally, it should be noted that σ_e is smaller the farther the final level is from the initial level.

The angular distribution of the scattered electrons after an excitation reaction tends to be isotropic when the fraction of energy lost by these electrons is large. In the opposite case, the distribution is analogous to that corresponding to elastic collisions: viz., an important forward scattering lobe and marked secondary lobes depending on the energy involved.

4.3.3 Excitation by ions or atoms

The excitation may be represented thus:

$$A^+ + B \rightarrow A^+ + B^*$$
$$A + B \rightarrow A + B^*$$

$$(4.4)$$

If the target particle (mass m_2) is at rest and the incident particle (mass m_1) has a kinetic energy E, the reaction threshold is

$$E_s = \frac{m_1 + m_2}{m_2} eV^*$$

that is to say, clearly higher than eV^* (cf. Sections 4.3.1 and 4.3.2).

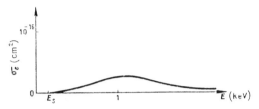

Fig. 4.4. Excitation by heavy particles

The increase in σ_e after this threshold is exceeded is much slower in this case than for electrons (Fig. 4.4): $(\sigma_e)_{max}$ is only reached at energies of some keV or some tens of keV. This phenomenon can be explained on the following basis. The probability of an inelastic reaction depends essentially on the time for which the distance between the particles is of the order of the "radius of action" of the atomic forces, that is $a \sim 10^{-8}$ cm. This time t is of the order of a/v where v is the relative velocity of the two particles. This should be compared with the time τ for an atomic transition of energy U; according to quantum theory $\tau \sim h/\Delta U$ ($\sim 10^{-15}$ sec). If $t \gg \tau$, the atomic structure will be progressively transformed to take account of the presence of the incident particle by means of an adiabatic change in the course of which the quantum state remains unaltered. On the other hand, if $t \approx \tau$ an instantaneous transition to another level will take place. If v increases, the duration of the interaction diminishes and with it the probability of a transition. The maximum for σ_e should therefore occur at $v \sim a/\tau$ of the order of 10^7 cm/sec. While for electrons this velocity corresponds to some eV, for ions it corresponds to some keV, which is in agreement with experience. The general character of the excitation curves is analogous to that for electrons, the maximum effective cross sections for excitation by atoms and molecules being, in general, of the same order as those for excitation by electrons.

4.4 Ionization

When an atom (or a molecule) has absorbed a sufficient amount of energy for one of its electrons to escape to infinity, the atom (or molecule) is said to have been ionized, its internal energy having increased by the ionization energy

$$\Delta U = eV_i.$$

Tables 1.2 and 1.3 give the potential V_i for single ionization (loss of the most loosely bound electron of the last shell) of various atoms and molecules. Naturally $V_i > V^*$. Once an atom (or molecule) has been ionized, it can be ionized again once or several times. The successive ionization potentials, $V_{i,n}$, become larger and larger: in effect, when a peripheral electron has been detached, the density of the negative electron cloud diminishes and the electric influence of the positive nucleus is felt more strongly by the other electrons; the cloud thus contracts about the nucleus and the remaining electrons are bound more tightly. Thus it can be seen why $V_{i,n}$ increases, while the corresponding effective cross section decreases.

When an incident particle has sufficient energy, it can eject an electron from an inner shell: thus ~ 10 keV are needed to ionize the K shell. During the subsequent rearrangement of the atom, the lost electron is replaced by an electron from a higher level. This transition is accompanied by the emission of a very high-energy photon which may in its turn ionize the same atom. Thus up to 5 electrons may be freed by a single incident particle: this is the Auger effect.

Futhermore, the electrons ejected from the inner shells of the atom often have a considerable energy and can themselves become effective ionization agents: in fact, they are more effective than the initial photon radiation.

The experimenter must be able to distinguish between the effects due to these secondary ionization photons or electrons and those due to the primary particle.

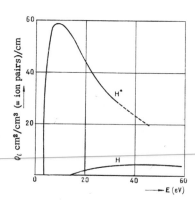

Fig. 4.5. Comparison of yields from excited and nonexcited hydrogen atoms ionized by electrons. $Q_i = n\sigma_i$ is the number of ion pairs created per cm of path of an electron in the gas at 1 mm Hg (cf. Section 2.6) (F. MANDL, *AERE, Rep. T/R 1006*, 1952)

In conclusion, it should be noted that, as opposed to ionized atoms, excited atoms can be ionized more easily than neutral atoms in the ground state (Fig. 4.5), this obviously being due to the fact that excitation has elevated the peripheral electron to a higher energy level, that is, to an orbit farther from the nucleus and therefore more loosely bound to it, and, having a larger surface area, the result is that the ionization threshold is reduced and the effective cross section is increased (cf. cumulative excitations, Section 4.3.1).

Note: A particular case of ionization occurs when the surplus electron is detached from a negative ion (neutral atom + electron); in this case $A^- \rightarrow A$.

4.4.1 Ionization by photons

The basic reaction

$$h\nu + A \rightarrow A^+ + e^-$$

represents photo-ionization and can take place when

or

$$h\nu \geqslant eV_i$$

$$\lambda(\text{Å}) \leqslant \frac{12,400}{V_i \text{ (volts)}}$$

This condition limits the photoelectric effect to the ultraviolet (U.V.) or X-ray regions of the spectrum (2000 to 3000 Å for alkaline metals; 500 Å for rare gases; cf. Tables 1.2 and 1.3). The curves for the effective cross sections are as shown in Fig. 4.6.

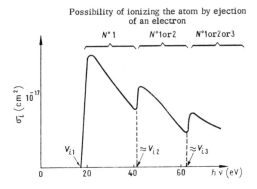

Fig. 4.6. Photo-ionization (or photoelectric effect)

The sharp rise in σ_i at certain values of the photon energy corresponds to the ejection threshold of one of the peripheral electrons. The probability of an ejection rises suddenly from zero to a finite value and this is additional to the probability of the ejection of the more loosely bound electrons.

Note that:

1. after the ionization threshold $V_{i,n}$ has been passed, σ_i increases rapidly to a maximum value which is lower the higher the order of ionization (cf. Section 4.4);

2. the shape of the curve between two successive ionizations is given approximately (for ultraviolet) by

$$\sigma_i = C \frac{\lambda^4}{\lambda_i - \lambda}$$

and for X-rays by

$$\sigma_i \propto \lambda^3 Z^4$$

Thus the maxima are less acute than for excitation (cf. Section 4.3.1). This is due to the fact that the conservation principles can always be satisfied thanks to the ejected electron;

3. the maxima in σ_i are of the order of 10^{-17} cm^2 or less;

4. σ_i is very small at high energies.

4.4.2 Ionization by electrons

The basic reaction equation is:

$$e^- + A \rightarrow e^- + A^+ + e^- \tag{4.6}$$

If the target is at rest and the incident electron has a kinetic energy E, the reaction can only take place if

$$E \geqslant eV_i$$

As can be seen from Fig. 4.7, the effective cross section increases rapidly once the threshold energy has been passed, as the conservation conditions are easily satisfied due to the ejected electron (cf. Section 4.3.2).

Certain sections of these curves can be represented by the following approximate analytical expressions:

$$
\begin{aligned}
Q_i &= ap(V - V_i) && \text{for } V_i < V \leqslant 2V_i \\
Q_i &= Q_m p[1 - e^{-b(V - V_i)}] && \text{for } V \leqslant V_m \\
Q_i &= p\,\frac{C_1}{VV_i}\ln\left(\frac{C_2 V}{V_i}\right) && \text{for } V > \text{several hundreds of eV}
\end{aligned}
\tag{4.7}
$$

where a, b, C_1 and C_2 are constants

p = pressure of target gas in mm of mercury
V = $(1/e) \times$ kinetic energy of incident electron
Q_m = Q_i maximum for $p = 1$ mm Hg
V_m = $(1/e) \times$ corresponding kinetic energy

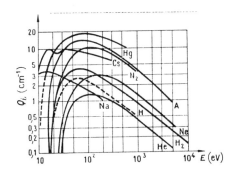

Fig. 4.7. Ionization by electrons (A. von ENGEL,
Handbook of Physics 21, Springer, 1956)

Note: Q_i is the number of ion pairs (one a positive ion and the other an electron) produced per centimeter of the incident electron's path in the target gas (at pressure p). This is often called the "ionization efficiency" (cf. Section 2.6).

The maximum values of σ_i are of the order of 10^{-16} cm^2 ($Q_i \sim 10$ to 20 cm^{-1}) and correspond, in general, to electron energies of the order of 100 eV (about 20 eV for alkaline metals).

Note the decrease with $(\log V)/V$ as for excitation (cf. Section 4.3.2).

After the collision one slow electron and one fast electron which carries off the major part of the kinetic energy not used in the reaction are generally present. The slow electrons have an approximately uniform angular distribution while the fast electrons tend to conserve the direction of the initial electron (cf. excitation collisions, Section 4.3.2).

4.4.3 Ionization by ions, atoms or molecules

$$\begin{cases} A^+ + B \rightarrow A^+ + B^+ + e^- \\ A\ \ + B \rightarrow A\ \ + B^+ + e^- \end{cases} \tag{4.8}$$

The notes detailed in Section 4.3.3 (excitation by ions and atoms) apply to this type of reaction: the maximum effective cross sections correspond to high kinetic energies (10^4 to 10^5 eV). However, after the threshold is exceeded, the increase is quasilinear as for ionization by electrons.

The accuracy of the results leaves much to be desired, but the efficiency of argon as an ionizing agent should be pointed out (Figs. 4.8 and 4.9).

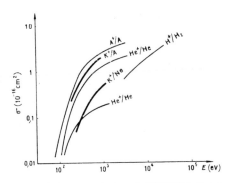

Fig. 4.8. Ionization by ions (A. ROSTAGNI, *Nuovo Cim.* 15 (2):117 (1938); 11, 34 & 99 (1934); W. WIEN, *Hdb. of Exp. Phys.* 14, Leipzig (1927). (The numerator in each "fraction" represents the test particle, and the denominator the target gas)

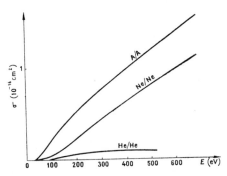

Fig. 4.9. Ionization by atoms (G. L. WEISSLER et al., *J. Opt. Soc. Am.* 42, 84 (1952); *Proc. Roy. Soc.* A, 220, 71 (1953)

Conclusion. In practice, electrons are the most efficient ionizing particles, followed by ions and, lastly, photons.

5 inelastic collisions (II): recombination, charge transfer, dissociation

5.1 Recombination

Recombination is the attachment of particles in the course of an encounter between a positive ion and an electron or between a positive ion and a negative ion. The ions can be atomic or molecular.

When describing this phenomenon, instead of using the concept of effective recombination cross section σ_r, that of the coefficient of recombination, α, is often applied, α being defined as the rate of decrease of positive (n^+) and negative (n^-) charges

$$\mathrm{d}n^+/\mathrm{d}t = \mathrm{d}n^-/\mathrm{d}t = -\alpha n^- \cdot n^+ \tag{5.1}$$

where n^- represents electrons or negative ions. The values of n are expressed in cm^{-3}; α is expressed in cm^3/sec.*

Comparing (5.1) with the formula defining the collisional frequency (Chapter 2), it can be seen that:

$$\alpha = \int_0^\infty v\sigma_r(v) f(v) \, \mathrm{d}v = \; <v \cdot \sigma_r(v)> \tag{5.2}$$

$$\approx \bar{v}\sigma_r(\bar{v})$$

where v = relative velocity of particles involved.

*The lifetime of ions, which, by definition, is equal to the inverse of the collisional frequency, will therefore, according to (5.1), be given by $T = 1/\alpha \, n^+n^-$.

α is a macroscopic quantity (representing a mean of microscopic quantities) which is more accessible to the experimenter than the cross section σ_r; σ_r decreases very rapidly as the velocities of the particles under investigation increase, and, since it is quite difficult to obtain monoenergetic beams at low energies, it is not easy to find σ_r as a function of v.

However, little is known about α either, because of the difficulties involved in measuring it. Most of what follows will therefore be purely theoretical, starting with the general concepts.

Ions of opposite sign are attracted to one another but the attractive force is not always sufficient to cause them to combine. As in the case of excitation and ionization, the probability of recombination depends on the ratio t/τ where t is the duration of the interaction, that is a/v = radius of target particle divided by velocity of test particle, and τ is the mean time necessary for the reaction to take place. τ obviously depends on the particular process of recombination. We shall, in fact, see that there are several such processes (excitation, photon emission, dissociation, etc.), each of which has a different value of α.

According to this reasoning, the probability of recombination depends on the type of particle involved since, whatever the type, neither a nor τ varies very much. On the other hand, a does vary considerably with the level of excitation of the atoms or molecules; α is clearly higher for excited particles.

5.1.1 Ion-electron recombination

We shall study in turn four types of recombination (there are perhaps others in addition).

5.1.1.1   Radiative recombination

$$e^- + A^+ \begin{array}{c} \nearrow A + h\nu \\ \searrow A^* + h\nu \end{array} \qquad (5.3)$$

The first reaction leads to an electron being taken into the ground level and to the emission of a photon of energy

$$h\nu = E_k - (-E_i) = E_k + E_i$$

where
E_k = kinetic energy of the electron
E_i = ionization energy of target (Fig. 5.1)

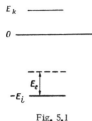

Fig. 5.1

The second reaction gives rise to a particle excited to level n. So that

$$h\nu = E_k + E_i - E_e$$

where E_e = excitation energy of level n.

Since E_k is, in general, distributed at random between all the electrons present, the recombination radiation covers a continuous spectrum limited on the low-frequency side. The probability of recombination decreases as the relative velocity of the particles increases; the intensity of the spectrum decreases towards higher frequencies.

In any case, the total effective recombination cross-section is very small and, as a whole, decreases with $1/E_k$ (that is $1/v^2$).

Table 5.1 gives values of σ_r calculated for proton-electron radiative recombination.

Table 5.1

E_e (eV)	0.034	0.07	0.13	0.28
σ_r (cm²)	2.7×10^{-19}	1.2×10^{-19}	0.54×10^{-19}	0.23×10^{-19}

Note: 0.034 eV corresponds to the ambient temperature. At this temperature

$$\alpha \approx v\sigma \approx 10^{-13} \, \text{cm}^3/\text{sec}$$

In general, effective cross-sections calculated for other ions are even smaller. Measured values are distinctly higher than those given above.

The direct attachment of electrons to neutral atoms defined by the following equation is a particular case of recombination:

$$e^- + A \to A^- + h\nu$$

The energy E_a of an e^--atom bond is called the electron affinity of the atom in question. It varies between zero and several volts.

It is positive for electronegative bodies (F, Cl) wishing to acquire electrons and negative for those which cannot attach them or which lose them easily (H, Li, Na) (electropositives).

The energy of the emitted photon is given by:

$$hv = E_a + E_k$$

The probability of an attachment taking place is, in general, even less than that of the previous reactions since there is not even a Coulomb attraction between the target and the test particles, and also the number of levels to which the electron can be attached is reduced to one in the majority of cases. This probability is measured by the coefficient of attachment, p, a dimensionless, macroscopic quantity (probability per collision).

p varies from 10^{-4} for Cl (electronegative) to 10^{-8} for paraffins.

5.1.1.2   Recombination with double excitation

$$
\begin{array}{c}
e^- + A^+ \rightarrow A^* \begin{array}{l} \nearrow A^+ + e^- \\ \searrow A + hv + hv' \end{array}
\end{array}
\tag{5.4}
$$

During the first stage, the incident electron is drawn into an excited state of the atom and the energy available raises another electron of the same atom to another excited level (cf. Auger effect or autoexcitation). After a certain time has elapsed, one of these electrons is ejected leaving the ion in its initial state (first possibility), or the two electrons fall to the ground state emitting two photons (second possibility).

5.1.1.3   Recombination in the presence of a third particle

$$^-e + A^+ + X \rightarrow A + X \tag{5.5}$$

If an electron encounters a particle X in the neighborhood of an ion A^+, it may communicate its energy to this particle and slow down sufficiently to recombine with A^+. Instead of being emitted in the form of photons the recombination energy, $E_k + E_i$, of this reaction is used to accelerate the third particle X.

The probability of this occurring obviously depends on the nature and density of the X particles.

5.1.1.4   Dissociative recombination

or

$$
\begin{array}{l}
e^- + A^+_2 \rightarrow A + A \\
e^- + AB^+ \rightarrow A + B
\end{array}
\tag{5.6}
$$

This reaction can take place in the course of a collision between an electron and a molecular ion. The two resultant atoms can be excited or nonexcited. The recombination energy (equal to the ionization energy of the molecule) is absorbed by dissociation, possible excitation and acceleration of the resultant atoms.

The effective cross section of this reaction is clearly greater than that for previous reactions. This can be explained as in Paragraph 5.1. In effect, the time τ for dissociation with or without excitation is of the order of 10^{-13} sec while it was about 10^{-8} sec for the emission of a photon (recombination accompanied by radiation). This gives coefficients of dissociative recombination of the order of 10^{-8} cm^3/sec.

5.1.1.5 Conclusion. The effective cross sections and electron-ion recombination coefficients decrease rapidly as the relative velocities of the particles (that is, the temperature of the gas under investigation) increase. For all recombination processes, α has values between 10^{-10} and 10^{-8} cm^3/sec (experimental results) for temperatures up to several thousand °K.

5.1.2 Ion-ion recombination

Three types of ion-ion recombination are known:

recombination with associated radiation (radiative recombination)

$$A^+ + B^- \rightarrow AB + h\nu \qquad (5.7)$$

mutual neutralization (exchange of charge without forming a molecule)

$$A^+ + B^- \rightarrow A^* + B^* \qquad (5.8)$$

three body recombination (X is generally an atom or molecule)

$$A^+ + B^- + X \rightarrow AB + X \qquad (5.9)$$

The first two phenomena are binary and therefore take place at low pressure (< 1 mm Hg).

As in the case of ion-electron collisions, the probability of an ion-ion radiative recombination is very small; the corresponding coefficient should not exceed 10^{-14} cm^3/sec. On the other hand, mutual neutralization with excitation of the resultant atoms gives $\alpha \approx 10^{-8}$ cm^3/sec. These two recombination coefficients are independent of the pressure and the ion concentration; the total

E

recombination coefficient will therefore be constant and of the order of 10^{-8} cm³/sec at pressures below 1 mm Hg.

The third recombination process is of some importance since two ions A^+ and B^- are seldom far from a third particle, X, able to absorb the energy resulting from the reaction. It is therefore to be expected that the probability of recombination will increase with the density of particles other than the ions A^+ and B^-, that is to say with pressure. This is exactly what J. J. Thomson demonstrated in 1924:

$$\alpha = \text{Const.} \, p \cdot T^{-5/2}$$

This theory remains valid up to pressures of the order of 1 atmosphere. Above this, the theory predicts that α will tend to a "saturation" value since the density of X particles becomes so great that recombination is practically certain for any encounter between a positive and a negative ion. However, this has not been borne out experimentally: after reaching a maximum value, of the order of 10^{-6} cm³/sec, the recombination coefficient decreases with $1/p$ when p, the pressure of the gas under investigation, is greater than about 1 atmosphere.

A theory put forward by Langevin in 1903 explains this phenomenon in the following manner. It has been seen (Section 5.1) that $\alpha \approx \bar{v} \, \sigma_r \, (\bar{v})$. At high pressures, σ_r is constant and of the order of magnitude of the area of the central cross section of the ions in question. On the other hand, the velocity $\bar{v}$ of an ion is equal to the product of the electric field of the nearest ion and its mobility in the gas under investigation. Now, according to the kinetic theory of gases, this mobility is inversely proportional to the pressure. Thus

$$\alpha = \frac{\text{Const.}}{p}$$

It is probable that at even higher pressures, α will again tend to the value corresponding to binary reactions only. The curve for $\alpha(p)$ will therefore be of the form shown in Fig. 5.2.

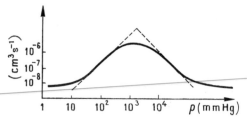

Fig. 5.2. Ion-ion recombination coefficients

The experimental results are in good agreement with each of these theories in the range for which each is valid.

Before concluding, it should be remembered that ion-ion recombination obviously assumes the presence of negative ions in the gas in question.

The negative ions are generally formed in one of two ways:

(a) By an electron becoming attached to an atom or a neutral molecule (cf. Section 5.1.1.1). Thus one can have

$$O^-, O_2^-, NO_2^-, NO_3^-, OH^-, H^-, Cl^-, Cl_2^-, F^-, C^-, CH^-, \text{ etc.}$$

But this is not always possible. Thus

$$H_2^-, N^-, N_2^-, He^-, Ne^-, A^-$$

have never been observed.

(b) By dissociation of a molecule. Examples:

$$e^- + O_2 \rightarrow O + O^-$$
$$e^- + O_2 \rightarrow O^+ + O^- + e^-$$

For further details see MASSEY, *Negative Ions* (1950, Cambridge).

5.1.3 Conclusion

Very little is known about the process of recombination. Broadly, it can be stated that:

1. over a wide range of pressure and temperature, the total coefficient of ion-ion recombination is a great deal larger than that of an ion-electron recombination for the same ion;

2. the probability of recombination decreases very rapidly with the velocity of the particles (or their temperatures);

3. the probability of radiative recombination is very small, but nevertheless sufficient to give luminosity to discharges which are only just maintained.

5.2 Charge transfer

5.2.1 Definition

$$\boxed{\overline{A}^+ + B \rightarrow \overline{A} + B^+}$$ (5.10)

A captures an electron and B loses one. Thus, in general

$$A^{n+} + B^{m+} \rightarrow A^{(n-1)+} + B^{(m+1)+}$$

Here, A and B can be either atoms or molecules.

5.2.2 Energy balance

Taking reaction 5.10 as an example, the energy balance equation may be written as follows:

$$\left.\begin{array}{l}\text{Total initial kinetic energy + ionization energy of } A \\ = \text{total final kinetic energy + ionization energy of } B\end{array}\right\} \quad (5.11)$$

In general, the ionization energies (E_i) differ little; as a result, the total kinetic energy varies very little in the course of the reaction. Furthermore, there is little exchange of impulse in the laboratory coordinate system, each particle more or less conserving its initial velocity.

The condition (5.11) defines a threshold energy

$$E_s = (E_i)_B - (E_i)_A$$

When $(E_i)_B > (E_i)_A$, the reaction can only take place above a certain minimum value of the relative velocity of the two particles. This is the case, for example, with H^+_1 in molecular hydrogen H_2 (Fig. 5.3).

The effective cross section for neutralization (capture of an electron), designated by σ_{10} or σ_{+0}, thus increases to a maximum, which is usually fairly high (10^{-15}cm^2 or more), and then decreases as the relative velocity of the particles increases (Fig. 5.3).

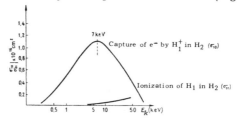

Fig. 5.3. Effective cross section for charge transfer by protons in hydrogen (E_k kinetic energy of H_1; H_2 at rest) (H. S. W. MASSEY & E. H. S. BURHOP, *Electronic and Ionic Impact Phenomena*, Clarendon Press, Oxford, 1952)

On the other hand, when $(E_i)_B \leqslant (E_i)_A$, the energy threshold is nil: σ_{10} already has a significant value at $E_k = 0$. This is true for He$^+$ in all gases (since the ionization potential of He is greater than that of other substances (Fig. 5.4), and for any atomic ion in its atomic gas $(E_s = 0)$.

These experimental results can be explained by means of very simple concepts analogous to those in Section 4.3.3 or 4.4.3 on excitation and ionization.

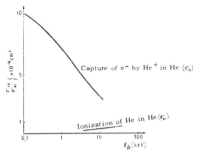

Fig. 5.4. Charge transfer of He⁺ ion in its gas
(MASSEY and BURHOP, *op. cit.*)

In this case, the variation in internal energy during the reaction is $\Delta E = E_s$. The time for this transition is $\tau \approx h/E_s$. If a is the mean radius of the particles and v is their relative velocity, then a maximum probability for the reaction (that is, a maximum effective cross-section) would be expected at

$$t/\tau = a\,E_s/vh \approx 1$$

Experiment shows that the relative velocity corresponding to σ_{max} does vary with E_s; in particular, when $E_s \leqslant 0$, this velocity is zero.

5.2.3 Equilibrium composition of a beam of fast particles

Let a beam of fast ions A^+ and atoms A be injected into a gas B. Very little of the beam is absorbed by elastic collisions. The only important reactions in this case are of the following type:

$$A^+ + B \to A\ \ + B^+ \quad \text{(charge transfer; } \sigma_{10})$$
$$A^+ + B \to A^{++} + B + e \quad \text{(ionization; } \sigma_{12})$$
$$A\ \ + B \to A^{++} + B + 2e\,\text{(ionization; } \sigma_{02})$$
$$A\ \ + B \to A^+\ + B + e \quad \text{(ionization; } \sigma_{01})$$
$$A^{++} + B \to A^+\ + B^+ \quad \text{(charge transfer; } \sigma_{21})$$
$$A^{++} + B \to A\ \ + B^{++} \quad \text{(transfer; } \sigma_{20})$$

During these reactions, the relative velocity v of the A particles varies only slightly, the ionization energy being small in comparison with the initial kinetic energy. Let N, n_0, n_1, n_2 be the densities of particles B, A, A^+ and A^{++} respectively. Then:

$$dn_0/dt = N\,v\,[n_1\,\sigma_{10} + n_2\,\sigma_{20} - n_0(\sigma_{01} + \sigma_{02})]$$
$$dn_1/dt = Nv\,[n_0\,\sigma_{01} + n_2\,\sigma_{21} - n_1(\sigma_{10} + \sigma_{12})]$$
$$dn_2/dt = Nv\,[n_0\,\sigma_{02} + n_1\,\sigma_{12} - n_2(\sigma_{20} + \sigma_{21})]$$

In equilibrium, all the expressions on the left-hand side are zero, thus giving a system of 3 simultaneous equations with 3 unknowns n_0, n_1, n_2 from which the ratios of the three species A, A^+, A^{++} can be deduced. These ratios are obviously independent of the initial composition of the beam but dependent on its velocity which influences the effective cross section.

Example: He in He gas (Fig. 5.5).

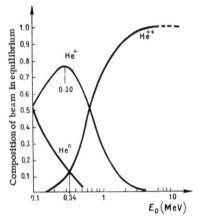

Fig. 5.5. Equilibrium composition of a beam
of He in He gas

From Fig. 5.5 it can be seen that the higher the velocity of the beam, the greater the proportion of highly ionized ions. This is a general result arising from the fact that the maxima of the effective cross sections are displaced towards higher energies as the degree of ionization increases.

Finally, note that the equilibrium composition of the beam is not established until several mean free paths have been traversed.

5.2.4 Conclusions

The high cross sections associated with charge transfer make this process one of the most important in ionized gases. One of the experimental difficulties arising due to this phenomenon is that, when heavy particles have been neutralized by charge transfer, they fly out to the walls since they can no longer be controlled by electric or magnetic fields. A useful application of the same phenomenon is the production of neutral, high-energy particles by neutralizing the ions after they have been accelerated in an electric field.

5.3 Dissociation

There is a fairly high probability of a molecule dissociating into two or more constituent components since the energy required for this to happen is rarely greater than 10 eV.

Dissociative recombination $(e^- + A_2^+ \rightarrow A + A)$ is a particular case of this (Section 5.1.1.4).

Dissociation may give rise either to neutral atoms or molecules or to charged particles of both signs:

$$e^- + CO \rightarrow C^+ + O^- + e^-.$$

The process can be accompanied by ionization

$$e^- + CO \rightarrow C^+ + O + 2e^-$$

or by attachment

$$e^- + CO \rightarrow C + O^-.$$

6   surface phenomena

6.1 Introduction

Until now we have not explicitly envisaged solid bodies in contact with the gas in which collisions are taking place.

This state of affairs occurs very frequently in the universe; for example, in stars and the atmosphere of planets.

On the other hand, it is still almost unknown in the laboratory. Except in experiments where certain particular reactions are studied, all artificial plasmas occupy such small volumes that the presence of the walls can rarely be neglected, and the less so the lower the pressure of the gas.

The surfaces of solid bodies act in various ways on the gases with which they are in contact. The following is a list of various processes:

A. *Primary or spontaneous emission*

—neutral particles due to the effect of heat (evaporation)
—charged particles

$\Big\{$ due to the effect of heat
due to the effect of an electric field (emission usually limited to electrons).

B. *Reflection of photons and neutral or charged particles of matter.*
In the case of ions and molecules, reflection may take place without change of state or accompanied by neutralization or ionization.

C. Secondary emission of neutral or charged particles from the solid under impact from charged or uncharged particles of matter or photons. Emission of X-rays by high-energy electrons.

D. Absorption of charged particles, neutral particles and photons

{ neutralization by disposal of charge
{ conservation of charge in the case of insulators

All these phenomena are localized in the surface molecular layers of the material forming the walls: on the one hand, normal particles rarely penetrate farther than a micron (e.g., penetration depth of 650 kV electrons in Al $\approx$ 0.6 mm; this is more penetrating than ions of the same energy but less penetrating than photons); on the other hand, primary or secondary particles emerging from the walls have even less energy and can only come from layers even nearer the surface.

Now the surface layer of a solid body is the least well defined part of it and the most difficult to control for the following reasons:

(a) from a mechanical point of view, it is very difficult to obtain and maintain a surface polished to better than 1μ;

(b) from a chemical point of view, it is very difficult to avoid oxidation of the surface and, more generally, adsorption of stray molecules which modify the nature of the surface.

All this makes it very difficult to study even the most elementary surface phenomena. For this reason, very little is known about them.

At the same time, the study of gas discharges has been, and still is being, hampered in many cases because of the little-known, variable and often determinative influence of the walls.

From a theoretical point of view, the problems are far from being solved. They are alleviated, of course, by quantum mechanics the laws of which are well known but often difficult to apply. Thus, in the case of practical insulating materials, often organic compounds, theory has advanced very little.

On the other hand, the theory of metals and their alloys has been the object of a large number of investigations (see F. SEITZ, *Modern Theory of Solids*, Masson 1949; A. H. WILSON, *Theory of Metals*, Cambridge, 1953), the results of which can be used to advantage in the study of gas discharges.

One of the essential concepts in this field is that of a potential barrier (or work function) in metals and conducting alloys.

It is known that the charge carriers responsible for the conductivity of metals are the valence electrons weakly bound to the atoms and able to move quasi-freely inside conducting solids. But these electrons cannot spontaneously leave the conductor because they are surrounded by a potential barrier. Inside the solid they are distributed between a series of discrete though finely separated energy levels which are all lower than the energy level of a free electron at rest in the empty space surrounding the metal (see Fig. 6.1). In this figure E_F is the Fermi level ($\simeq 10$ eV) and is the highest energy level occupied at absolute zero.

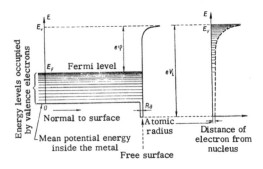

Fig. 6.1. Energy diagram of valence electrons in a good conductor at 0°K. By way of comparison, the energy levels of an electron gravitating about an isolated nucleus are given on the right-hand side of the figure as a function of its distance from the nucleus. E_v is the potential energy of an electron in vacuum

The work function is defined by

$$e\varphi = e(E_v - E_F)$$

which is the energy that must be supplied to an electron in the highest level (Fermi level) in order that it shall be able to leave the solid. The potential barrier φ is, in general, of the order of several electron volts and is the result of the attraction between atoms outside the surface and the charge reflected in the surface (the image charge). Note that $\varphi < V_i$.

φ varies a little with T but it is very sensitive to surface impurities (generally oxides).

This theoretical model is very well substantiated by experiment. Today a great deal of general experimental and theoretical data relating to metals and their alloys is available (see KNOLL, *Material and Processes in Electron Devices*, Springer, 1959). These materials should therefore be used, wherever possible, in preference to other solids.

6.2 Spontaneous emission

6.2.1 Evaporation

There is a continuous exchange of atoms and molecules between a solid body and the atmosphere by which it is surrounded, these atoms and molecules being the same as those constituting the solid. These particles exert a vapor pressure which makes up part of the whole of the ambient pressure. After a sufficiently long time, a statistical equilibrium is set up which is characterized by a saturation pressure in the region of the solid. The saturation pressure increases rapidly as a function of temperature. It is greater for volatile substances (iodine, mercury, potassium, sodium, etc.) than for others.

6.2.2 Degassing or desorption

This is the name given to the phenomenon whereby solids or liquids emit atoms or molecules of a different nature which are initially present in these solids or liquids in one form or another (e.g., as occlusions).

This degassing is greatly accelerated by heating. That is why, in careful experiments, enclosures are always baked, using resistances sheathed in asbestos or flames, to around 400° or 500°C.

6.2.3 Thermionic emission

6.2.3.1 *Emission of electrons.* When a metal is heated, the kinetic energy of certain electrons (those which participate in conduction) is increased. The number of electrons able to surmount the potential barrier and escape from the metal therefore also increases. The density of the electron emission current is given by Dushman's formula:

$$j_s = A T^2 \exp\left(-e\varphi/kT\right)$$

j_s is called the saturation current density since, in principle, it is the maximum current which can be extracted from the surface of the metal at temperature T. This relation demonstrates that emission increases very rapidly with temperature. For tungsten at 2500°K, $j_s \approx 0.3$ amp/cm^2. In fact there is never complete saturation since j_s also depends on the magnitude of the electric field present at the surface of the emitting material. In effect, this field alters the shape of the potential barrier and Fig. 6.2 shows how the barrier may be lowered by an amount ΔE: this is called the Schottky effect, as it was he who demonstrated that the dependence of the emission current on the field was as follows

$$j = j_s \exp\left(e^{3/2} E^{1/2}/kT\right)$$

This formula remains valid up to field strengths of 10^6 V/cm [*Proc. Roy. Soc.*, 120 A, 432 (1928)].

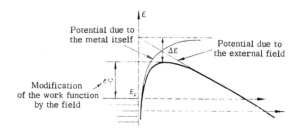

Fig. 6.2. Schottky effect. Potential barrier (for negative charges) in the presence of a positive electric field at the surface

6.2.3.2 Emission of ions. Similarly, heated metals may emit positive or negative ions in accordance with Dushman's formula. But the corresponding work function is greater, by several eV, than that for electrons. Thermionic emission is therefore only significant close to the fusion temperature. Evaporation is then very intense and at 2800°K, tungsten (W) only emits one positive ion per 4000 atoms. Certain salts and oxides of alkaline metals have very much higher ion emissions, a fact exploited in the Kunsman anode.

Remarks:

1. The velocity distribution of emitted particles is "Maxwellian;" escape velocities can take all values between zero and infinity.

2. If the electrons emitted by a heated surface are not absorbed by an adjacent electrode raised to a sufficiently positive potential, they form a cloud in front of the emitting cathode, this cloud constantly exchanging particles with the heated surface. This negative space charge forms yet another potential barrier for the escaping electrons.

3. The energy which a conduction electron must acquire in order to be able to overcome the potential barrier of the emitting body must be supplied by the thermal energy of the emitter.

6.2.4 Field emission (or cold emission)

When an electric field has been set up at the surface of the metal in an outward direction, the form of the potential barrier is modified as shown in Fig. 6.2.

Now quantum mechanics predicts that, under these circumstances, the conduction electrons in the upper energy levels close to the Fermi level have a finite probability of passing through (not surmounting) the barrier. This is known as the tunnel effect.

The density of the field emission current is given by the Fowler-Nordheim equation:

$$j = 6 \times 10^{-6} \frac{\sqrt{E_F / e\varphi}}{E_F + e\varphi} X^2 \exp\left(\frac{-6.8 \times 10^7 \varphi^{3/2}}{X}\right)$$

where:

X is the electric field in V/cm

E_F is the Fermi level in eV

$e\varphi$ is the work function in eV

j is the current density in amp/cm^2

Several amp/cm^2 can be obtained in this way with fields of 10^7 to 10^8 V/cm.

As in the case of thermionic emission, this current density can be greatly increased by the presence of surface layers of absorbed gases or oxides.

Field emission differs from thermionic emission in that:

1. The emitted electrons all have very low velocities. The velocity distribution shows a sharp peak close to zero.

2. The work performed in escaping is practically nil; the kinetic energy which may be acquired by the electrons comes from the applied electric field.

3. The emission current is independnet of temperature.

6.3 Reflection

Certain charged and uncharged particles of matter incident on the surface of a solid (or walls of an enclosure) undergo simple reflection, analogous to an elastic collision. In the same way, photons are partly reflected or scattered by the walls. If the enclosure has a crystalline structure, diffraction or selective reflection phenomena can be observed. Moreover, certain ions are able to capture an electron and to re-emerge in the form of neutral particles in either the ground or an excited state.

Conversely, neutral particles penetrating into the walls may be ionized before escaping again.

6.4 Secondary emission

When the incident particles possess a sufficient energy, they may eject atoms or molecules or groups of atoms or molecules from the walls. This is called sputtering (pulverization).

Ions may also be emitted under the impact of high-energy, charged or uncharged particles on the walls.

Very high-energy electrons may even cause X-rays to be emitted. However, we shall ignore all secondary emission phenomena except for those involving the emission of electrons due to the effects of photons (photoelectric effect), electrons, ions and neutral, charged or uncharged particles.

6.4.1 Action of electrons

When a beam of monoenergetic electrons is incident on a solid wall, the latter will emit electrons some of which will simply be the primary electrons reflected without loss of energy (Paragraph 6.3). But the walls also eject a certain number of secondary electrons per incident electron, the average value of this number being greater or smaller than 1. As shown in Fig. 6.3, the secondary electrons, for the most part, have an energy of the order of 10 eV.

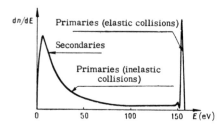

Fig. 6.3. Energy spectrum of electrons emitted by a surface of silver bombarded with electrons of 160 eV (dn = number of electrons with an energy in the interval E to $E + dE$)

Between the two extreme peaks is a group of electrons with intermediate energies probably made up of electrons reflected inelastically.

The coefficient (or power) of secondary emission, δ, is defined as the ratio of the total number of electrons leaving the walls to the number of incident electrons. (Secondary emission therefore, by convention, includes reflected electrons as well as true secondary electrons.)

The elementary process of secondary emission is still not well understood. Nevertheless, experiment has verified that a threshold energy equal to the work function of the surface bombarded $E_s = e\varphi$ does in fact exist. This means that the peak at small energies only appears for $E > E_s$.

Figure 6.4 shows the variation in δ as a function of the energy of the primary electrons, the latter being incident perpendicular to the surface.

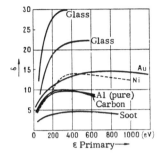

Fig. 6.4. Coefficient of secondary emission. (H. BRUINING, *Physics and Applications of Secondary Electron Emission*, Pergamon Press, 1954)

δ depends on the nature and the state (mechanical and crystallographic) of the bombarded surface, and also on the impurities present in the surface. It is higher for polished than for rough surfaces ($\delta < 1$), for insulators ($\delta \sim 5$) than for metals ($\delta \sim 0$ to 2), for the oxides of alkaline earths ($\delta \sim 10$) than for other substances.

The maxima occur at energies in the range 100 to 1000 eV (see Fig. 6.4 and Table 6.1).

Table 6.1. Maximum secondary emission coefficient for various metals

Metal	δ_{max}	E (eV)
Ag.	1.5	800
Al	1	300
Au.	1.5	750
Cd.	1.1	400
Cu.	1.3	600
Fe.	1.3	350
Mo.	1.25	375
Ni	1.3	550
Pt	1.8	800
W.	1.4	700

Secondary emission is more intense the greater the angle of incidence of the primary electrons (Fig. 6.5), but it does not depend on the temperature.

The energy distribution for the secondary electrons depends only slightly on the angle of incidence, θ, for the primary electrons; however, if φ is the angle the trajectory of a secondary electron makes with the normal, the angular distribution varies with cos φ (i.e., maximum in a direction normal to the surface).

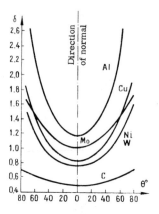

Fig. 6.5. Variation of δ as a function of the angle of incidence of the primary electrons. (F. PREVOT, in *Theory and Technics of Accelerators*, V1, INSTN, 89 (1959)

Finally, the time between the arrival of the primary electron and the departure of the secondary electrons does not exceed 10^{-12} sec.

The majority of these experimental results can be explained if one accepts that:

(a) the incident electrons penetrate to a greater or lesser degree depending on whether they have larger or smaller energies and on whether they are incident at a smaller or larger angle of incidence;

(b) over the whole of their paths in the solid they impart energy to electrons which are then scattered in all directions;

(c) those of the secondary electrons which have gained a sufficient quantity of energy at a sufficiently small distance from the free surface are able to escape from the latter; it has been shown that secondary electrons come from depths less than about 30 Å.

Malter effect. Values of δ greater than 1000 can be obtained by lightly oxidizing an aluminum surface (producing a thin film of Al_2O_3) and then depositing on it a layer of Cs_2O. The latter becomes positively charged and strongly attracts the aluminum electrons.

6.4.2 Action of ions

Ions, like electrons, may cause secondary emission from surfaces on which they are incident.

However, they differ primarily in that the threshold energy is double that of electrons:

$$E_s = 2e\varphi$$

This is due to the fact that besides the secondary electron which is liberated, the ion itself leaves the surface taking with it a second electron which neutralizes the ion.

But this time the energy available for this reaction is equal to the kinetic energy of the incident ion plus its ionization energy eV_i. The latter is liberated at the moment at which the ion is neutralized. Since, in general, $V_i \gg \varphi$, the available energy is almost always greater than the threshold energy.

Despite this, the yield or power of secondary ion emission (γ_{ion} = number of secondary electrons/number of incident ions) is generally < 1 for energies below 1000 eV.

γ_{ion} increases with the energy of the primary ion up to a maximum of several unit this being reached at energies of the order of 100 keV.

6.4.3 Action of excited atoms (Penning effect)

Excited atoms incident on a surface may lose their excitation energy, eV^*, to an electron which can then escape if V^* is greater than φ (collision of the second kind). Naturally metastable atoms are more effective due to their long lifetimes. The coefficients of secondary emission may reach 1 for these atoms (e.g., helium on pure Mo, Ni or Mg).

Note that the kinetic energy of the incident atoms plays a negligible part in this case. It is generally a great deal smaller than the excitation energy.

6.4.4 Action of neutral atoms in the ground state

These only dispose of their kinetic energy which must be in the region of several keV before secondary emission is significant.

6.4.5 Action of photons (photoelectric effect)

This phenomenon is characterized by a threshold; the wavelength or frequency denoted by the subscript s

$$\boxed{h\nu_s = e\,\varphi} \quad \text{or} \quad \boxed{\lambda_s(\text{Å})\,\varphi\,(\text{volts}) = 12{,}400}$$

where
    ν = frequency of incident electromagnetic (E.M.) wave
    λ = its wavelength

F

The critical wavelength λ_s generally falls in the ultraviolet. Beyond this threshold, the maximum velocity of the emitted electrons is given by the relation

$$E = \tfrac{1}{2} m_e v_{\max}^2 = h\nu - e\varphi$$

Figure 6.6 shows the energy spectrum for the secondary electrons.

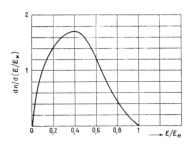

Fig. 6.6. Energy spectrum for photoelectrons. $E_M = h\nu - e\varphi$ is the kinetic energy of the fastest secondary electrons. (A. von ENGEL and M. STEENBECK, *Electrical Discharges*, Springer, Berlin, 1932-34)

Figure 6.7 represents the variations in the photoelectric emission coefficient, γ_p, as a function of the incident wavelength

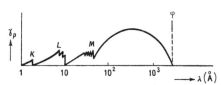

Fig. 6.7. Photoelectric emission coefficient (number of electrons emitted per incident photon). (A. von ENGEL, *Ionized Gases*, Clarendon Press, Oxford, 1955)

The left-hand part of this diagram may be recognized as representing the probability of ionization (cf. Fig. 4.6) of the atoms in the surface being bombarded (K, L, M shells).

The right-hand part corresponds to the secondary photoelectric emission; the phenomenon is obviously connected with those electrons least bound to the atomic structure ($\varphi < V_i$). The corresponding maximum occurs between 100 and 1000 Å.

The effectiveness of photons as a source of secondary emission depends on the same factors as in the case of electrons, ions and atoms.

γ_p is higher for rough surfaces (cf. Paragraph 6.4.1) than for polished surfaces and it depends on the polarization of the incident light.

γ_p is rarely greater than 1 since a great part of the incident light is reflected or transformed into heat.

Remarks. For a given wavelength, secondary emission is proportional to the number of incident photons, that is to say, to the intensity of the source of irradiation.

Note on the potential of an isolated electrode surrounded by an ionized gas. When the bombarded surface is an insulator, or an electrically insulated conductor, it will be charged positively or negatively depending on the circumstances. If it is sufficiently insulated, it will eventually assume a potential such that a statistical equilibrium is established between the current emitted and the current received.

6.5 Absorption and adsorption

Some of the photons or charged or uncharged particles of matter bombarding a material surface will be absorbed; part of the energy carried by the incident particles is expended in heating this surface, the other part being removed by secondary particles or radiation.

Even when they have no energy, neutral particles, atoms or molecules may become attached to the surface of a solid body due to the effect of the van der Waals forces of molecular attraction; adsorption takes place.

Adsorption is greater the greater the effective surface presented to the gas. Porous charcoal and silica gel are particularly notable in this respect. It is also more effective at low temperatures. The following table shows the adsorbing properties of charcoal.

Cm^3 (NTP) of gas absorbed per cm^2 of charcoal

Gas	$0°C$	$-185°C$
H_2........	4	135
CO_2.......	21	190
N_2........	15	155
O_2........	18	230

In addition, certain metals (tantalum, titanium, tungsten) when hot have the property of absorbing molecules of the gas by which they are surrounded (sorption). This property is applied to the titanium pump.

See DUSHMAN, *Scientific Foundations of Vacuum Techniques,* J. Wiley, 1949.

7   transport phenomena

7.1 Introduction

In the previous chapters we limited ourselves to elementary phenomena involving two, or occasionally three, particles. We have seen that the nature of these phenomena depended on the velocity and the position (impact parameter) of the particles present. To take account of the random distribution of the positions of molecules in a real gas, we introduced the concept of probabilities of effective cross sections and we saw that these depended on velocity. But up till now, even when we considered a beam of incident ''test'' particles, we assumed, a restrictive hypothesis, that it was monoenergetic and that we knew its velocity: all numerical data have therefore been presented in diagrams with the parameter velocity (or energy) as abscissa.

In reality the situation is a great deal more complex than this. The number of particles present is always enormous, and, in general, all sorts of reactions are taking place at the same time. Under these conditions, not only are the molecules distributed throughout the useful volume, but also their velocities are distributed throughout velocity space and the distribution varies in space and time as long as equilibrium has not been reached.

If the distribution of velocities and position cannot be known at any given moment, instead of using microscopic quantities (effective cross section, etc.), one is forced to introduce macroscopic quantities describing properties of the whole assembly of molecules. Thus the recombination coefficient α (Chapter 5) defines the pattern of distribution of ions in a given gas with a given pressure, ''temperature'' and ion concentration.

Since the velocity distribution is so little known, this system falls down because it is not always clear whether results obtained under one set of experimental conditions are applicable under other conditions (generally equally poorly defined).

The difficult problem of the actual ion velocity distribution function therefore arises once more.

Disregarding the uncertainty relations of quantum mechanics, let us assume that the velocity and position of each molecule at a given moment are known. It is quite out of the question to follow the history of each molecule; there are far too many of them.

All that can be done is to define a distribution function $f(\mathbf{w}, \mathbf{r}, t)$ representing the mean density of particles at a point $\mathbf{r}$ at time t and having a velocity $\mathbf{w}$.

More exactly, the number of molecules of type i which, at an instant between t and $t + \mathrm{d}t$, have coordinates in the intervals x to $x + \mathrm{d}x$, y to $y + \mathrm{d}y$ and z to $z + \mathrm{d}z$ and have components of velocity between w_x and $w_x + \mathrm{d}w_x$, w_y and $w_y + \mathrm{d}w_y$, w_z and $w_z + \mathrm{d}w_z$ (Fig. 7.1) will be given by the equation

$$\mathrm{d}N_i = f_i(\mathbf{w}, \mathbf{r}, t)\, \underline{\mathrm{d}w}\ \underline{\mathrm{d}r} \tag{7.1}$$

where

$\underline{\mathrm{d}w} = \mathrm{d}w_x\, \mathrm{d}w_y\, \mathrm{d}w_z$

$\mathbf{r}$ = position vector of components x, y, z

$\underline{\mathrm{d}r} = \mathrm{d}x\, \mathrm{d}y\, \mathrm{d}z$

The element of density will be $\mathrm{d}n_i = \mathrm{d}N_i/\mathrm{d}r$.

In an assembly made up of different types of molecules, each type will be characterized by a function f_i.

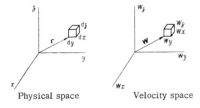

Physical space   Velocity space

Fig. 7.1

If f_i does not depend on $\mathbf{r}$, the gas of type i is said to be homogeneous. A steady state* is characterized by the absence of t in

*Editor's Footnote: French:—régime permanent. In common with other English published work relating to gas kinetic theory the following terms are used in this text: the *steady state* is defined by $\partial f / \partial t = 0$; if $\partial f / \partial \mathbf{r} = 0$ the state is said to be *uniform* or *homogeneous*; when the flux of any property vanishes everywhere a state of *complete equilibrium* is said to prevail (when in a state of complete equilibrium $\partial f / \partial t = \partial f / \partial \mathbf{r} = 0$).

the expression for f. Finally, if f depends only on the absolute value of the velocity and not on its direction, the velocity distribution is said to be isotropic; in this case

$$dn_i = F_i(w, \mathbf{r}, t)\, dw(w, \mathbf{r}, t) \qquad (7.2a)$$

or

$$F_i = 4\pi\, w^2 f_i \qquad (7.2b)$$

Example: parallel monoenergetic beam in vacuum

$$f = C\, \delta(\mathbf{w} - \mathbf{w_0})$$

where δ is the Dirac function.

In a general way, the form of the distribution will be determined by the initial conditions of the experiment, by the external forces acting on the molecules and by the reciprocal reactions between the latter, that is to say, their collisions.

Boltzmann established a differential equation for f which takes all these factors into account and which, in principle, means that f can be determined in the general case.

If f is known, the frequency of various types of collisions can be calculated and consequently the intensity of certain elementary phenomena, such as the emission of radiation, for example, can be found.

The local macroscopic properties of the gas in question can similarly be deduced from the distribution function as follows:

density

$$n(\mathbf{r}, t) = \int_{\mathbf{w}} f\, dw$$

mean velocity of fluid

$$\mathbf{v}(\mathbf{r}, t) = (1/n) \int_{\mathbf{w}} \mathbf{w} f\, dw$$

mean kinetic energy of particles with mass m

$$\mathcal{E}(\mathbf{r}, t) = (1/n) \int_{\mathbf{w}} \tfrac{1}{2} m\, w^2 f\, dw$$

In these formulas, the integrals cover the whole range of possible velocities.

These formulas contain the expressions for the three first moments of the function f. Taking the upper orders of moments, the expressions for the pressure, energy flux (or quantity of heat), etc., can be found.

In a steady state all these quantities are, by definition, independent of t. In a state of complete equilibrium a further condition is satisfied: all the mean fluxes are nil (particle, energy, momenta flux, etc.). In the general case, this is not true and knowledge of f leads to the transport phenomena for particles (diffusion), momentum (viscosity), charge (electric current), kinetic energy (thermal conductivity), etc., which tend to equalize conditions at all points in space.

In the following, we shall establish Boltzmann's equation, find the appropriate expression for f for Maxwellian equilibrium, study the theory underlying the principal transport phenomena and finally consider in detail the problems of diffusion and mobility of charges which are of great importance in the field of electric gas discharges.

7.2 Boltzmann's equation

For the sake of simplicity, let us consider the case of a pure gas containing only one type of molecule. Let m be the mass of these molecules, $m\gamma$ the external force acting on them and f the velocity distribution. If it is assumed that the molecules do not impinge upon one another and that they have no influence at a distance, then it can be reasoned that at any instant t, the unit volume $\underline{dr}\,\underline{dw}$ enclosing the point $(\mathbf{r}, \mathbf{w})$ of the generalized space and velocity coordinates is occupied by

$$f(\mathbf{r}, \mathbf{w}, t)\,\underline{dr}\,\underline{dw}$$

molecules. After time dt, these molecules will have been displaced by $\mathbf{w}dt$ and their velocity will have altered by γdt; provided $\partial\gamma_i/\partial w_i = 0$, they will occupy the same volume $\underline{dr}\,\underline{dw}$ but about the point $(\mathbf{r} + \mathbf{w}dt, \mathbf{w} + \gamma dt)$. The number of molecules, which is unchanged, can then be written with the previous conventions as

$$f(\mathbf{r} + \mathbf{w}dt, \mathbf{w} + \gamma dt, t + dt)\,\underline{dr}\,\underline{dw}$$

Now the kinetic theory of gases assumes that, if the molecules have no effect upon one another at a distance, they will nevertheless impinge two at a time and thus abruptly change velocity (hypothesis of binary collisions). Under these conditions, the group of molecules displaced from $\mathbf{r}$ to $\mathbf{r} + \mathbf{w}dt$, the velocity of which changes from $\mathbf{w}$ to $\mathbf{w} + \gamma dt$ in the interval t to $t + dt$, will lose a certain number which change velocity but at the same time it will gain a certain number of other molecules for the same reason and at the expense of other groups of molecules.

The variation in the initial number of molecules will obviously be proportional to $d\underline{r}\ d\underline{w}\ dt$. Let us call $(\partial f/\partial t)_c$ the coefficient of proportionality. Then:

$$[f(\mathbf{r} + \mathbf{w}\ dt, \mathbf{w} + \gamma\ dt, t + dt) - f(\mathbf{r}, \mathbf{w}, t)]\ d\underline{r}\ d\underline{w} = (\partial f/\partial t)_c\ d\underline{r}\ d\underline{w}\ dt$$

or

$$\boxed{\frac{\partial f}{\partial t} + \mathbf{w} \cdot \frac{\partial f}{\partial \mathbf{r}} + \gamma \cdot \frac{\partial f}{\partial \mathbf{w}} = \left(\frac{\partial f}{\partial t}\right)_c} \tag{7.3}$$

This is Boltzmann's equation where

$$\frac{\partial f}{\partial \mathbf{r}} = \text{grad}_{\mathbf{r}}\ f = \mathbf{i}\ \frac{\partial f}{\partial x} + \mathbf{j}\ \frac{\partial f}{\partial y} + \mathbf{k}\ \frac{\partial f}{\partial z}$$

$$\frac{\partial f}{\partial \mathbf{w}} = \text{grad}_{\mathbf{w}}\ f = \mathbf{i}\ \frac{\partial f}{\partial w_x} + \mathbf{j}\ \frac{\partial f}{\partial w_y} + \mathbf{k}\ \frac{\partial f}{\partial w_z}$$

If this equation is written in the form

$$\frac{\partial f}{\partial t} = -\mathbf{w}\ \frac{\partial f}{\partial \mathbf{r}} - \gamma \cdot \frac{\partial f}{\partial \mathbf{w}} + \left(\frac{\partial f}{\partial t}\right)_c$$

it can be seen that the variation in the distribution function at a given point $(\mathbf{r}, \mathbf{w})$ is due to:

1. diffusion of molecules to points in space where there are fewer of them;

2. variations in their velocities due to the effect of external forces applied to them;

3. collisions between molecules.

It can be shown that the influence of collisions appears in the last term in the form of a multiple integral of a function of f (an integrodifferential equation). Even in this form Boltzmann's equation is fairly difficult to solve but it becomes more complicated still when the reciprocal actions of molecules and ions in very dense or highly ionized gases must be taken into account.

7.3 Thermodynamic equilibrium

The steady state is characterized by the fact that collisions do not modify the velocity distribution function: $(\partial f/\partial t)_c = 0$.

In explaining this equation and in solving it for a uniform gas $(\partial f/\partial r = 0)$ with no external forces acting $(\gamma = 0)$, Boltzmann arrived at an expression for f which Maxwell had already found by a different method:

$$f(w) = n\,(m/2\,\pi kT)^{3/2}\exp(-mw^2/2\,kT)\qquad(7.4)$$

This is the Maxwell-Boltzmann distribution. In addition

$$F(w) = 4\,\pi\,n\,(m/2\,\pi kT)^{3/2}\,w^2\exp(-mw^2/2\,kT)$$

where
  n = number of particles per unit volume
  m = mass of a particle
  k = Boltzmann's constant = 1.38×10^{-16} (CGS)
  T = thermodynamic temperature

These relations show that, in equilibrium:

1. the particles are randomly distributed over the whole space (uniform distribution),

2. their velocities are uniformly distributed in all directions (isotropic distribution).

These two conditions are combined under the name of molecular chaos. The following can be calculated:

(a) most probable velocity

$$w_p = \sqrt{2\,kT/m}\qquad(7.5)$$

(b) mean velocity

$$\overline{w} = \frac{1}{n}\int_0^\infty wf\,\mathrm{d}w = \sqrt{8\,kT/\pi\,m}\qquad(7.6)$$

(c) mean square velocity

$$c = \sqrt{\overline{w^2}} = \sqrt{3\,kT/m}\qquad(7.7)$$

These velocities are in the ratio

$$1\ :\ 1.13\ :\ 1.23.$$

Note in passing that the mean kinetic energy of a particle is

$$E = \tfrac{1}{2}\,m\overline{w}^2 = \tfrac{1}{2}\,mc^2 = 3\,(\tfrac{1}{2}\,kT)$$

that is, $\tfrac{1}{2}\,kT$ for each degree of freedom (the law of equipartition of energy for thermodynamic equilibrium).

Now the velocity of a particle of mass m and energy E is given by

$$v(\text{cm/sec}) = \frac{1.79}{10^6}\sqrt{E(\text{eV})/m(\text{g})} = 5.9 \times 10^7 \sqrt{E\, m_e/m}$$

Thus, for example, at 0°C the mean square velocity of H_2 molecules in thermodynamic equilibrium is $\approx 1.8 \times 10^5$ cm/sec.

It can be shown that this equilibrium is always established eventually provided that the particles are not subjected to forces arising from outside (that is to say, those not due to their own field), that the enclosure is maintained at a constant temperature T and that the total number of particles is large enough ($\lambda \ll D$).

If this equilibrium is instantaneously disturbed, it will be reestablished after a relaxation time, τ, which is of the order of magnitude of the time for collisions between two particles. In fact, it is the transfer of energy and momentum which occurs in the course of these collisions which permits equipartition of the total energy and the reestablishment of molecular chaos.

It is clear that:

$$\tau = 1/\theta = 1/n\,\overline{v}\sigma$$

(all this applies for particles of the same type).

For a gas at N.T.P., $\tau \approx 10^{-9}$ sec.

In an assembly of different species of molecules in equilibrium, the distribution functions corresponding to the different species only differ by a factor; the thermodynamic temperature T is the same for all species.

Despite these limitations the Maxwell-Boltzmann distribution is important since:

(a) it represents to a first approximation the actual distribution;

(b) under certain circumstances, at least one of the various species of molecules present will obey the M-B law: for example, in the Lorentz model, the neutral molecules and heavy ions.

Remarks:

1. The presence of a magnetic field does not modity the Maxwell distribution even in the case of charged particles.

2. In the presence of a field due to external forces arising from a potential $\omega(r)$, the distribution function at equilibrium takes the form

$$F = \text{Const.}\ \exp(-\omega/kT)\exp(-mw^2/2\,kT)$$

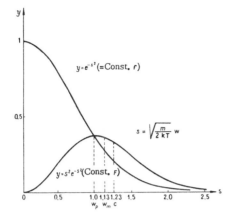

Fig. 7.2. Maxwell–Boltzmann distribution

7.4 Transport equations

Instead of solving the Boltzmann equation for f and then taking
moments of this function to obtain the macroscopic properties of
the gas, it is possible to attempt to modify Boltzmann's equation
itself so that the desired property can be deduced. Let us denote
this property which depends on the parameters defining the state
of each molecule (mass, velocity, etc.) by A. Multiply Boltzmann's
equation by $A \, \underline{\mathrm{d}w}$ and integrate over the whole of velocity space.
After various manipulations, we find that

$$
\frac{\partial(n\overline{A})}{\partial t} = -\frac{\partial}{\partial \mathbf{r}}\left(n\,\overline{A\mathbf{w}}\right) + \\
n\left\{\overline{\frac{\partial A}{\partial t}} + \mathbf{w}\cdot\overline{\frac{\partial A}{\partial \mathbf{r}}} + \gamma\cdot\overline{\frac{\partial A}{\partial \mathbf{w}}}\right\} + \int_{\mathbf{w}} A\left(\frac{\partial f}{\partial t}\right)_c \mathrm{d}w
\tag{7.8}
$$

where

$$
\partial/\partial \mathbf{r} = \nabla_{\mathbf{r}}
$$

and where all the underlined expressions represent a mean of all
velocities.

This is the transport equation of the property A.

This equation relates to the unit volume of gas surrounding
the position vector $\mathbf{r}$ at a time t.

The first term represents the variation in time of the macroscopic property

$$n\,\overline{A} = \int A\,f\,\underline{dw}$$

This variation is due to:

1. the flux of particles towards the interior and exterior of the element of volume in question $\left(-\partial\,(n\,\overline{A\,w})/\partial\,r\right)$;

2. variations in A with the parameters of state of each molecule: time, position, velocity, etc. (first bracketed term);

3. collisions (last term) occurring in the local element of volume; all molecules coming from outside this volume y give up any surplus they have in the property with respect to the mean of this property for the element in question.

7.4.1 Approximation to the transport equation

Consider the case of a steady state $(\partial/\partial t = 0)$; let us assume that the external forces are zero $(\gamma = 0)$ and that A is a scalar property independent of r: these are conditions which are fairly generally fulfilled. The transport equation then becomes

$$\mathrm{div}\,(n\,\overline{A\mathbf{w}}) = \int_{\mathbf{w}} A\,(\partial f/\partial t)_c\,\underline{dw}$$

where, integrating over some volume V with surface Σ,

$$\int_V \mathrm{div}(n\,\overline{A\mathbf{w}})\,d\tau = \int_\Sigma n\,\overline{A\mathbf{w}}\cdot d\mathbf{S} = \int_V d\tau \int_{\mathbf{w}} A\,(\partial f/\partial t)_c\,\underline{dw}$$

$\mathfrak{n}$ is the unit vector normal to Σ at P pointing outwards.

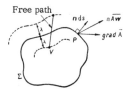

Free path

Fig. 7.3

To find a more explicit expression for the last term, the following reasoning may be applied.

The surface of separation Σ is constantly crossed in both directions by molecules undergoing thermal agitation. The property

$\overline{A}$ is not the same on one side of the surface Σ as it is on the other. The molecules therefore transport a greater flux of this property in one direction than in the other. The resultant flux can easily be determined.

In effect, each molecule at every instant has a mean value A of the property in question considered at the point at which it underwent its last collision. But, on the average, the ends of a free path passing through Σ are at distances $+\lambda$ and $-\lambda$ from Σ. Therefore a molecule leaving V through a point P carries off an amount $\overline{A}$ $(\mathbf{P} - \lambda \mathbf{n})$ while a molecule entering through the same point brings with it an amount $\overline{A}(\mathbf{P} + \lambda \mathbf{n})$.

Now since the distribution of velocities is Maxwellian, the mean particle flux per unit time per unit surface is $n\overline{w}/4$, in either direction. Finally, the net flux of the property $\overline{A}$ across Σ in an outward direction is

$$\frac{n\overline{w}}{4} \left[\overline{A}(\mathbf{P} - \lambda\mathbf{n}) - \overline{A}(\mathbf{P} + \lambda\mathbf{n}) \right] dS = \frac{-n\overline{w}\lambda}{2} (\text{grad } \overline{A} \cdot d\mathbf{S})$$

per unit time, whence

$$\int_\Sigma n \, \overline{A}\mathbf{w} \cdot d\mathbf{S} \approx - \int_\Sigma \tfrac{1}{2} n\overline{w}\lambda \, \text{grad} \ \overline{A} \cdot d\mathbf{S}$$

Since we have made no restrictions on V or Σ, we can conclude that the flux in the property A per unit of surface normal to this flux is

$$\boxed{n \, \overline{A}\mathbf{w} \approx - \tfrac{1}{2} n \, \overline{w}\lambda \, \text{grad} \ \overline{A}} \tag{7.9}$$

It is important to note that $\overline{w}$ is the mean of the absolute values of $\mathbf{w}$; $\mathbf{w}$ is the resultant of a mean velocity of motion of the fluid and a thermal agitation velocity which is generally a great deal larger than the former. $\overline{w}$ is thus practically the mean thermal agitation velocity which, as is known, is proportional to $\sqrt{T/m}$. On the other hand, since the product $n\lambda = 1/\sigma$ is independent of the density n, the latter takes no part in transport.

Note 1. The above reasoning and formulas are not valid if $\lambda \ll$ dimensions of the enclosure (high density) and λ grad $\overline{A} \ll \overline{A}$ (small difference between the values of A at two adjacent points).

Note 2. The transport equation shows that any difference between the properties of a gas at two points in the same enclosure tends to be compensated by a flux of particles between these two points.

7.5 Applications

7.5.1 Thermal conductivity

The property transported in this case is the thermal energy of a molecule, that is to say $mc_v\ T$. The heat flux is given in one dimensional space by

$$Q \approx -\tfrac{1}{2}\,n\overline{w}\lambda mc_v\,\mathrm{d}T/\mathrm{d}x = -K\mathrm{d}T/\mathrm{d}x \qquad (7.10)$$

$K = \tfrac{1}{2}\,n\,\overline{w}\,\lambda\,mc_v$ is the thermal conductivity.

7.5.2 Viscosity

Viscosity is the resistance exerted by one layer of fluid on an adjacent layer of fluid moving with a higher velocity.

By definition, this force (R) is the momentum transferred per second from the molecules of the second layer to those of the first. Let u be the velocity of motion of the layers parallel to each other and to the axis OZ ($\perp Ox$).

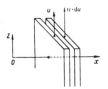

Fig. 7.4. The viscosity force R is parallel to the velocity u

The property transported in this case will be the mean momentum per molecule, mu. Whence

$$R \approx -\tfrac{1}{2}\,n\,\overline{w}\lambda m\,\mathrm{d}u/\mathrm{d}x = \eta\,\mathrm{d}u/\mathrm{d}x \qquad (7.11)$$

$\eta = \tfrac{1}{2}\,n\,\overline{w}\,\lambda\,m$ is called the coefficient of viscosity.

It can be seen that

$$K/\eta\,c_v = \text{Const.}$$

7.5.3 Diffusion

Let a gas be composed of two molecular species with densities n_1 and n_2 respectively at a homogeneous temperature T and subject to a uniform pressure

$$p = (n_1 + n_2) kT = nkT$$

If n_1 and n_2 are not constant over the volume under consideration, there will be a flux of molecules from each point to points where the concentration in that type of molecule is lower. The property under consideration in this case is the density. If we make $v_i = \overline{w_i}$, the flux $\Phi_i = n_i v_i$ of particles of type i will be given by

$$n_i \Phi_i \approx - \tfrac{1}{2} n_i \overline{w_i} \lambda_i \operatorname{grad} n_i$$

or

$$\boxed{\Phi_i \approx - \tfrac{1}{2} \overline{w_i} \lambda_i \operatorname{grad} n_i = - D_i \operatorname{grad} n_i} \qquad (7.12)$$

$D_i = \tfrac{1}{2} \overline{w_i} \lambda_i$ is called the diffusion coefficient.

Since $n_1 + n_2 = n = $ Const., a flux of type 1 is compensated by an equal and an opposite flux of molecules of type 2; thus $D_1 = D_2$ (when $\overline{w_1}\lambda_1 \neq \overline{w_2}\lambda_2$ there will also be transport of all the molecules in an overall motion to compensate for the difference between D_1 and D_2).

Note. The above calculations are far from being rigorous. However, results based on more elaborate approximations of Boltzmann's equation only differ by factors close to 1. In all events, the principal elements of the formula remain the same.

8   diffusion

In the previous chapter, we saw that, if one of the macroscopic properties of the gas was not distributed uniformly throughout the volume under investigation, a mean flux of this property appeared which tended to make conditions uniform at all points:

$$\text{Flux of property } A = -\text{Const. } n\,\overline{w}\lambda \text{ grad } \overline{A}$$

In a composite gas there is an equation of this type for each kind of particle. It should be remembered that it is a macroscopic equation with the implication that a very large number of the particles of the type in question are present, these being frequently in collision with other particles of the same or a different kind.

It should also be noted that the definition or the determination of λ is not always easy. Essentially, the m.f.p. between two collisions is that distance such that the molecule acquires the mean value of the property under consideration at the point of collision. (In the case of "billiard balls" there is no ambiguity.)

In the particular case of the diffusion of a cloud of particles in a given gas, we thus arrive at the following definition for the diffusion coefficient:

$$D \approx \overline{w}\,\lambda \; (\overline{w}\lambda/3 \text{ is often quoted})$$

In the majority of cases, the molecules we shall have to consider are displaced not merely due to the effect of a concentration gradient but under the action of a force, generally an electric or magnetic force.

Now a molecule subjected to an external force and surrounded by a gas acquires a velocity determined by its mobility in this gas as well as by the force applied. The two phenomena of diffusion and mobility are intimately connected and this is why they will be dealt with in two successive chapters.

8.1 Consequences of transport theory

Diffusion equation. In a general way, when a steady state has not been set up, the variation in the density of particles of a given type is given by the equation

$$\partial n / \partial t = - \operatorname{div}(n \, \mathbf{v})$$

(i.e., the transport equation for $A = 1$; $\mathbf{v}$ = velocity of motion = $\bar{w}$), or

$$\boxed{\partial n / \partial t \approx + D \, \nabla^2 n} \quad \text{(if } D = \text{Const.)} \tag{8.1}$$

Isotropic diffusion of a group of molecules. If, at time $t = 0$, there are N molecules at the origin O of coordinates the density of such particles at a distance e from this origin O at time t is given by the relation

$$\boxed{n = \frac{N}{(4 \, \pi \, Dt)^{3/2}} \exp(- r^2 / 4 Dt)} \tag{8.2}$$

obtained from the diffusion equation above, with

$$\nabla^2 n = \frac{\partial^2 n}{\partial r^2} + \frac{2}{r} \frac{\partial n}{\partial r}$$

Mean square distance travelled by a molecule. The distance travelled by a particle diffusing in a gas is a random function of time: it varies depending on the collisions undergone by the particle in time t.

This distance can easily be deduced from the equation given below or from the theory of fluctuations:

$$\boxed{\bar{r^2} = \frac{1}{N} \int_{r=0}^{\infty} r^2 \cdot 4 \, \pi r^2 \, n \, \mathrm{d}r = 6 \, Dt} \tag{8.3}$$

The factor 6 is replaced by 4 or 2 for 2 or 1 dimensional space respectively.

G

Note that the actual distance covered is

$$l = vt \gg \sqrt{\overline{r^2}}$$

Diffusion in the presence of a constant external force (forced diffusion). When the external force applied to each molecule is not large enough to impart a velocity comparable with the velocity due to thermal agitation (or a higher velocity), the resultant motion can be considered as the sum of a normal diffusion motion and a slow movement of the assembly of particles. The distribution of velocities at every point remains Maxwellian to a first approximation. In this case it can be shown that the drag velocity $v = |\overline{w}|$ is proportional to the force F (see Chapter 9)

$$v = MF, \text{ where } M = \text{mobility} \qquad (8.4a)$$

and that the relation between M and D is

$$D/M = kT \qquad \text{(Einstein; 8.4b)}$$

8.2 Experimental results (for neutral gases)

The expression for D obtained above does not predict any variation with concentration c. In fact, experiments carried out at N.T.P. show that D increases slightly with c ($c \propto$ partial pressure of the particles under consideration).

Moreover, v is proportional to $T^{1/2}$ and λ to $1/n$ or T/p so that we should have

$$\boxed{D = \text{Const. } T^{1.5}/p} \qquad (8.5)$$

where p is the total ambient pressure.

In practice the exponent of T is between 1.75 and 2.

Finally it should be pointed out that diffusion coefficients are of the order of 1 cm²/sec at N.T.P.

8.3 Charged particles

The case of ions (+ or -) is not very different from that of neutral particles. However, it has been calculated that the diffusion of ions in their own neutral gas is 4 or 5 times smaller than that of neutral molecules. This can be explained by the fact that the m.f.p. for ions is smaller than that of neutral molecules. In effect, the maximum distance for an ion-neutral molecule interaction is greater than that for molecules reacting with one another since the ions can induce electric dipoles in molecules at a distance, these dipoles then reacting with the ions.

The diffusion coefficient for electrons is several thousands of times greater than those for ions and neutral particles, their velocity and their m.f.p. being much greater than in the case of heavy particles.

As opposed to the case of ions, there is generally no simple relation between the diffusion coefficient and the electron mobility. The drag velocity for electrons subjected to an external force is usually so large that the resultant velocity distribution is no longer Maxwellian and the drag velocity is not even proportional to the applied force.

8.4 Ambipolar diffusion

When ions and electrons are present in equal concentrations at a point, they each tend to diffuse with their respective diffusion velocity. Since electrons diffuse more rapidly than ions, the latter tend to remain behind thus creating a positive space charge and a field which tends to retain the electrons (Fig. 8.1). The latter are thus decelerated and, eventually, particles of both signs diffuse with the same velocity.

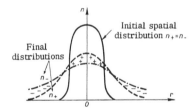

Fig. 8.1. Ambipolar diffusion

Let E_s be the electric field created in this way by the separation of the charges, $\mu = v/E_s$ the mobility of a charged particle and $\Phi = nv$ the mean particle flux; for the ions, for example

$$\Phi_+ = n_+ \mathbf{v}_+ = -D_+ \nabla n_+ + \mu_+ \mathbf{E}_s n_+$$

or

$$\mathbf{v}_+ = -(D_+/n_+) \nabla n_+ + \mu_+ \mathbf{E}_s$$

Similarly, for the electrons

$$\mathbf{v}_- = -(D_-/n_-) \nabla n_- - \mu_- \mathbf{E}_s$$

If it is assumed that $n_+ \approx n_- \approx n$ at all points, then (by dividing by μ_+ and μ_- and adding) we obtain:

$$\mathbf{v} = \mathbf{v}_+ = \mathbf{v}_- = - \frac{D_+ \mu_- + D_- \mu_+}{\mu_+ + \mu_-} \cdot \frac{\nabla n}{n}$$

The coefficient

$$D_a = \frac{D_+ \mu_- + D_- \mu_+}{\mu_+ + \mu_-} \qquad (8.6)$$

is called the ambipolar diffusion coefficient.

Remarks:

1. The above is only valid if the charge density of the two signs of charge is sufficiently high for the space to be charged significantly, otherwise it can not be assumed that $n_+ \approx n_-$.

2. As has been seen, the introduction of the concept of mobility is not always justified in the case of electrons.

When it is,

$$\mu_- \gg \mu_+$$

and

$$D_a = (k/e)\,(T_e + T_i)\,\mu_+$$

[note the introduction of T_e (electron temperature) $\neq T_i$ (ion temperature)].

If $T_i \gg T_e$, $D_a \approx D_+ =$ diffusion coefficient of the ions alone.

If $T_e = T_i$, $D_a \approx 2\,D_+$.

8.5 Diffusion of charged particles in a magnetic field

In a homogeneous magnetic field of induction **B**, a free particle of mass m and charge e will be subject to uniform motion in the direction of **B** and to rotational motion about this direction with constant angular velocity $\omega = eB/m$ and radius of gyration ρ (= Const./ω).

It can be seen from Fig. 8.2 that the m.f.p. changes from λ to a value of the order of ρ. Now according to Section 8.1, the diffusion coefficient is proportional to the square of the m.f.p. $(\overline{r^2} = N\rho^2)$ or, in this case, inversely proportional to ω^2. An exact calculation gives

$$D_\perp = \frac{D_0}{1 + (\omega\tau)^2}$$

for transverse diffusion. τ = time interval between two successive collisions.

Fig. 8.2. Diffusion in
a magnetic field

The coefficient of longitudinal diffusion obviously remains unchanged

$$D_{||} = D_0$$

This demonstrates the advantage of employing magnetic fields in order to confine charged particles.

8.6 Diffusion of space charge

When charged particles of the same sign subject to motion due to thermal agitation are concentrated at a point, they tend to become distributed uniformly throughout the space by two processes:

(a) normal diffusion (diffusion of concentration), or
(b) repulsion between charges of the same sign (which is independent of the thermal agitation and of collisions).

9 mobility

It has been found that at the center of a gas subjected to a low-intensity electric field, the heavy ions acquire a constant mean velocity (drag velocity) which depends on the field, the pressure and also on the nature of the ions and the gas.

This phenomenon is reminiscent of the motion of ions in an electrolyte or electrons in metals or forced diffusion of neutral gas molecules (Section 8.1).

It is obvious that in all these phenomena collisions with the surrounding molecules play an essential role in the establishment of a constant velocity (conversely, in vacuum the velocity of charged particles increases linearly as a function of time if the applied force is constant).

Equation (8.4a) can be used to find this drag velocity in the case of ions of charge e subjected to an electric field E by making $F = eE$, and hence

$$v = (D/kT)\, e\, E$$

The mobility μ is then defined as

$$\boxed{\mu = v/E} \quad [= \; Me, \text{ cf. (8.4a)}] \tag{9.1}$$

and is thus given by

$$\frac{eD}{kT} = \frac{ev\lambda}{kT}$$

However, this reasoning is only valid for ions in thermal equilibrium with the ambient gas (see theory of diffusion); furthermore, it is obscure and does not indicate clearly the role of collisions. We shall therefore study other methods which are more concrete and which will be compared with experimental results for heavy ions and electrons.

9.1 Heavy ions

9.1.1 Elementary theory

Let us consider a neutral gas in which ions of charge e and mass M similar to that of the neutral molecules are dispersed, the whole being in a uniform electric field E. If the field E is weak and the density of neutral particles large, the ions will not have time between collisions to acquire an energy sufficient to cause inelastic collisions. On the other hand, elastic collisions with the neutral molecules will be very numerous and, as the masses are very similar, the transfer of energy will be considerable and will lead to the establishment of thermodynamic equilibrium whereby the velocities of the ions and neutral molecules will be distributed in accordance with Maxwell's law corresponding to a temperature T.

Note that:

1. in the case in question (the density of ions being low in comparison with that of the neutral molecules), there are few ion-ion collisions and they do not play an important part;

2. the equilibrium is only thermodynamic to a first approximation since, unlike the neutral molecules, the ions are subject to a drag velocity $v = |\bar{w}|$ different from zero (but assumed small compared with the mean velocity of thermal agitation, $\bar{w}$).

To find v, note that, in the interval of time $\tau = \lambda_t/\bar{w}$ which, on the average, separates two successive collisions between an ion and a neutral molecule, the ion covers a distance

$$s = (eE/2 M) \tau^2$$

in the electric field. (Note the absence of any term in τ; in each collision, the ion loses on the average all the drag velocity it has acquired; this is the hypothesis of thermodynamic equilibrium between the ions and the neutral molecules.)

The mean drag velocity is therefore

$$v = s/\tau = (e\lambda/2 M\bar{w}) E$$

More rigorous reasoning taking into account the statistical distribution of the m.f.p. leads to

$$v = (e\lambda/M\bar{w}) E \tag{9.2}$$

that is to say, to a mobility

$$\mu = e\lambda/M\overline{w}$$

or alternatively

$$\mu = (e/M\overline{w}^2)\,(\lambda\overline{w}) \approx eD/kT$$

Note:
At a given temperature, $\lambda = 1/n\sigma = \text{Const.}/p$ where n and p are the density and kinetic pressure of the neutral molecules. Hence

$$\boxed{v = \text{ Const. } (E/p)} \qquad (9.3)$$

The above expression contains one of the most important experimental parameters for discharges in gases:

$$E/p \text{ or } \lambda E \qquad (\lambda \sim 1/p)$$

which is the average amount of potential energy lost or kinetic energy, W, gained by an ion between two collisions.

9.1.2 Experimental results

Numerous experimental results confirm the above theory to a first approximation.
First, in most gases at N.T.P., the mobility of the majority of the ions with unit positive or negative charge is of the order of 1 to 10 (cm/sec)/(V/cm); and second, it has been shown experimentally that, at constant temperature, $\mu p \approx \text{Const.}$ This is, of course, due to the fact that under these conditions

$$\mu = \text{Const. } \lambda/\overline{w} = \text{ Const. } T^{1/2}/p$$

On the other hand, the elementary theory is contradicted by a large number of other results as discussed below.

1. μ is a function of the mass M of the ions and the mass M_0 of the neutral molecules

$$\mu = \text{Const. } (\text{I} + M_0/M)^{1/2}$$

and not Const./M. This formula was obtained by Langevin by taking into account the persistence of the drag velocity of an ion after a collision. It is well substantiated by experiment (Fig. 9.1).
2. μ is largely independent of T.

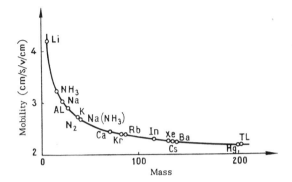

Fig. 9.1. Variations in the mobility of positive ions in N_2 as
a function of their mass. (J. D. COBINE, *Gaseous Conductors*,
Dover, 1957, p. 37)

3. The mobility μ^- of negative ions is systematically slightly
greater than that of positive ions, μ^+. This can be explained by the
fact that, during part of their existence, negative ions are simply
electrons the mobility of which has been seen to be very much
higher than that of heavy ions.

4. The experimental values for the mobility are systematically
lower than the theoretical values by a factor of 1/4 to 1/5. To
explain this, the following processes are invoked:

(a) The attachment of neutral molecules to positive ions, the
masses of which are therefore increased sharply.

(b) The attraction between the ions and the dipoles that they
induce in adjacent neutral molecules with which they would not
otherwise have reacted; this attraction brakes the ions and diminishes their mobility (cf. Section 8.3).

(c) Charge transfer between the (fast) ions and (slow) neutral
molecules. The energy acquired by the ion is carried off by it
when it has become neutral; it is therefore lost by the ion group.

Fig. 9.2. Attachment of molecules
to a positive ion

5. Finally, with intense fields and low densities (E/p large), the
energy acquired by an ion between two collisions is no longer
negligible with respect to the energy of thermal agitation, and the
hypotheses of the elementary theory are no longer satisfied. In
effect, the mobility $\mu = v/E$ is no longer independent of the electric
field, or, in other words, the drag velocity v is no longer proportional to E/p.

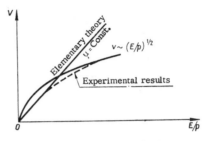

Fig. 9.3. Drag velocities for ions

For $E/p >$ several tens of (V/cm)/mm Hg,

$$v = \text{Const.} (E/p)^{1/2} \tag{9.5}$$

This relation is equally valid for the electrons (provided that E/p does not exceed several (V/cm)/mm Hg); we shall therefore deduce it in the following section which deals with electrons.

9.2 Electrons

9.2.1 Elementary theory

The enormous difference between the masses of electrons and ions gives rise to considerable differences in the behavior of the two kinds of particles in the same ambient gas.

An electron loses much less energy than an ion when it is involved in an elastic collision with a neutral molecule (Section 3.2.4). As a result, even at very low values of E/p, the mean energy of the electrons is well above the thermal energy of the molecules of the ambient gas.

Consequently, the concepts of thermal equilibrium of the electrons with the gas or of a Maxwellian velocity distribution are no longer applicable.

The velocities of an electron due to thermal agitation and to drag are large compared with the velocity of neutral molecules due to thermal agitation.

However, for the sake of simplicity, we shall assume that the mean velocity of thermal agitation of the electrons, $\bar{w}$, remains large compared with their mean drag velocity, v:

$$\bar{w} \gg v$$

and that the distribution of velocities for the electrons does not vary much with E/p so that the mean values are characteristic of the behavior of the system as a whole.

Besides this, provided E/p is large enough for inelastic collisions to occur, it can be assumed that an electron loses a fraction K = Const. of its energy, $\tfrac{1}{2}mw^2$, in each collision with a neutral molecule. Since $(\overline{w}/\lambda)\cdot dt$ such collisions take place in time dt, the kinetic energy lost by an electron in this time will be

$$K(\tfrac{1}{2}\,m\overline{w}^2)\,(\overline{w}/\lambda)\,dt$$

In a steady state, this loss is compensated by the energy gained from the electric field

$$e\,E\,v\,dt$$

In short, the electrical potential energy is constantly transformed into kinetic energy of motion of the electrons and then, because of collisions, into energy of thermal agitation of the electrons and molecules.

Setting the two expressions given above equal to one another, and taking into account that

$$v = (e\lambda/m\overline{w})\,E$$

we find that

$$v \approx (K/2)^{1/4}\,(e/m)^{1/2}\,(E\lambda)^{1/2} = \text{ Const. } (E/p)^{1/2} \tag{9.6}$$

In this relation, m and λ are the mass and m.f.p. of electrons.

If K, m and λ are replaced by the corresponding quantities for ions, we obtain an expression of the same form but with different coefficients (Section 9.1.2, No. 5).

Example: e^- in He with $p = 1$ mm Hg and $E = 3$ V/cm;

$$K = 2\,m/M = 2.8 \times 10^{-4}, \quad \lambda_e = 5.10^{-2}\ \text{cm}$$

Hence:

$$\overline{w} = 1.5\cdot10^8\ \text{cm/sec}\ (4\,\text{eV})\,;\ \ v = 2\cdot10^6\ \text{cm/sec}\,(\ll \overline{w})$$

Note. The concept of mobility has no meaning in this case since $v/E = $ Const. $E^{-1/2}$, which depends on E.

9.2.2 Experimental results

Experimental results are in good agreement with the elementary theory for $E/p <$ several (V/cm)/(mm Hg).

After this point v increases more rapidly than $(E/p)^{1/2}$. This can be explained by inelastic collisions which, beyond this value, can take place between electrons and neutral molecules. After a collision of this type, an electron will move off again in the direction of the field with a velocity which is practically zero; it rapidly acquires a large velocity parallel to E. Successive elastic collisions tend to reduce this velocity to the mean value given by (9.6), but a subsequent inelastic collision will interrupt this process so that the mean velocity (between two inelastic collisions) remains higher than that given by (9.6).

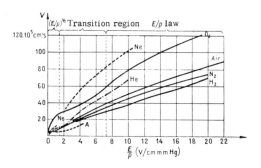

Fig. 9.4. Velocity of diffusion of electrons in different gases. (N. E. BRADBURY and R. A. NIELSON, *Phys. Rev.* **49**, 338 (1936) and **51, 69** (1937); R. A. NIELSON, *ibid.*, **50, 950** (1936)

The critical value of E/p is lower for molecular gases than for atomic gases (1 to 2 V/cm/mm Hg) because of the high probability of exciting molecular vibrations, this requiring an energy of the order of 1 eV.

At high values of (E/p), V as a whole varies linearly as a function of E/p and the idea of mobility is applicable once more. The value of the latter will be several tens or hundreds of thousands of times greater than that of the ion mobility (cf. Section 9.3).

9.3 Electrical conductivity of gases

Let us consider a gas containing not only neutral molecules but also positive ions and electrons at the same low, homogeneous concentrations: $n_i = n_e = n$.

The above results show that if an electric field is applied, which is not too high, the ions and electrons will undergo uniform motion parallel to E and in reverse directions with velocities v_i and v_e respectively.

The total current density is then

$$\mathbf{j} = n_i \, e \, \mathbf{v}_i - n_e \, e \, \mathbf{v}_e = ne \, \mathbf{E}(\mu_i + \mu_e)$$

But it has been seen that $\mu_e \gg \mu_i$ (in so far as one can speak of μ_e). Therefore:

$$\mathbf{j} \approx + nc \, \mu_e \, \mathbf{E}$$

Hence, the electrical conductivity essentially due to the electrons is given by

$$\sigma = j/E = ne \, \mu_e$$

It can be seen from this that σ increases with the charge concentration n, at least as long as this is small compared with the density of neutral molecules.

Important note: In all that went above (except Section 8.6), we neglected the interactions between charged particles. This is justifiable so long as the density is low. If it is not, collisions between charged particles and the electric field due to this must be taken into account. Finally, when E/p becomes large enough for ionization to occur, variations in the resulting charge density should also be taken into account. This is generally the case for discharges in gases.

Gases are, in general, very good insulators. However, under certain circumstances, they can be made to pass an electric current. In the following chapters we shall apply the concepts we have already derived to the principal types of discharge. They are many and various, but all are characterized by the presence of free charges and an electric field.

The electric field can be applied by electrodes either inside or outside the gas enclosure. This field can be steady or alternating, at low or high frequency. As to the electric charges, they may be produced in the volume of the gas or at the surface of the electrodes if these are inside the enclosure. The charges produced in this way can multiply under the action of the field if this is sufficiently large: the discharge current then increases in intensity. In certain cases, the internal multiplication of the charges is such that an external ionization agent has no effect. The discharge is then said to be self-sustaining, as opposed to nonselfsustaining discharges which are interrupted as soon as the external ionizing agent (electromagnetic or particle radiation, heat, etc.) ceases to act.

The pressure of the gas is an important parameter in every case and can significantly modify the characteristics of a discharge.

This chapter will be devoted to nonselfsustaining discharges with continuous current and a steady state. To simplify theoretical investigations, the electrodes will be considered to be plane, parallel and infinite (one dimensional geometry in x), separated

by d and entirely surrounded by gas (Fig. 10.1). We shall investigate the characteristics

$$V = f(x), \quad E = f(x), \quad n = f(x), \quad j = f(V)$$

where
   V = electric potential (V)
   E = field (V/m)
   n = charge density (C/m³)
   j = current density (A/m²)

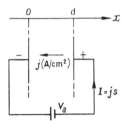

Fig. 10.1

10.1 Production of charges on electrode surfaces

To make electrodes emit electric charges it is necessary, for example, to heat them (thermionic emission) or to bombard them with ultraviolet light (photoelectric emission, see Chapter 6). These charges can be set in motion by an electric field; but their motion will depend on the obstacles they meet, that is to say, the pressure of the ambient gas. We shall consider in turn the cases of low and high pressures.

10.1.1 Electron emission at low pressure

Let us take the most usual case whereby one of the electrodes (anode) is raised to a potential V_a with respect to the other at a potential $V_0 = 0$ and heated to the point at which it emits an electric current of density j_s A/m² (Dushman's law) with an initial electron velocity of v_0 m/sec.

At every point, the velocity v of electrons of mass m and charge $-e$ is given by

$$-e (V_0 - V) = \tfrac{1}{2} m (v^2 - v_0^2) \tag{10.1}$$

According to the law of conservation of charge, in a steady state the current density is everywhere the same and is given by:

$$j = + n e v = \text{Const.} \qquad (10.2)$$

(this density cannot exceed the saturation value $j = j_s$).

The electric potential V obeys Poisson's law $\nabla^2 V + 4 \pi \rho = 0$, which can be written (in CGS ESU)

$$\frac{d^2 V}{dx^2} = 4 \pi n e \qquad (10.3)$$

since the charge density is $\rho = - ne.$

The boundary conditions are defined by

$$V_{x=0} = 0 ; \qquad V_{x=d} = V_a$$

Using the above equations it is possible to determine the unknowns n, v, j and V. The electric field is then given by $E = dV/dx$ (like the current j, it is taken to be positive in the direction from the anode to the cathode).

If it is assumed that j is not limited (that is to say, that the cathode is an inexhaustible source of electrons), solution of the system of equations above leads to the results represented in Fig. 10.2 for the case when $v_0 = 0$.

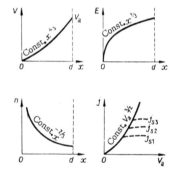

Fig. 10.2. Characteristics of space charge limited emission with $v_0 = 0$
(in vacuum)

In this case, the current density is given by Child's formula:

$$j = \frac{1}{9 \pi} \left(\frac{2 e}{m} \right)^{1/2} \frac{V_a^{3/2}}{d^2} \quad \text{(CGS ESU)} \qquad (10.4)$$

Naturally, this equation is only valid as long as

$$j \ll j_s$$

If j_s increases, j remains constant (determined by V_a and d) and the approximation (10.4) is more exact. This is said to be a space charge limited region.

When V_a is fairly large, all the electrons emitted by the cathode are absorbed by the anode and, whatever V_a may be, $j = j_s$. The emission is then limited by temperature. The curves in Fig. 10.2 are no longer valid and are gradually transformed into those in Fig. 10.3 (solutions to (10.1), (10.2) and (10.3) with $n \approx 0$, this approximate equality arising from the hypothesis that V_a is large). Note that E = Const. and V = Const. x.

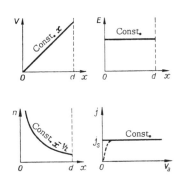

Fig. 10.3. Characteristics of cathode limited emission with $v_0 = 0$ (in vacuum)

In fact, the electrons are emitted with a mean initial velocity v_0 which, in general, is small compared with their final velocity close to the anode, but is not zero.* The most remarkable consequences of this in the space charge region are:

1. The charge density n is no longer infinite at $x = 0$.

2. The field E is no longer zero at $x = 0$.

3. The minimum in the potential, $- V_m$, occurs at a small positive distance, x_m, from the cathode (Fig. 10.4).

Fig. 10.4. Space charge limited emission (in vacuum). Influence of initial electron velocity

* See BLANC-LAPIERRE et al., *General Electronics* (Dunod) Appendix III; P. A. LINDSAY, "Velocity distribution in electron streams," *Advances in Electronics and Electron Physics,* XIII (1960).

H

Beyond this point, the system behaves as if there were a potential difference $V_a + V_m$ between the anode and a virtual cathode at x_m.

When the emission is limited by the temperature, the charge density at the cathode ceases to be infinite and has a value of j_s/ev_0.

States intermediary to those of space charge and temperature limitation are complex but, since they are rarely encountered in practice, we shall not deal with them at length here except to point out the dotted lines in Figs. 10.2 and 10.3.

10.1.2 Electron emission at medium or high pressure

In the presence of a gas with neutral molecules, the motion of the electrons is no longer given by Eq. (10.1) but by Eq. (10.5)

$$v = + \mu E = + \mu \, dV/dx \tag{10.5}$$

where μ is the mobility of an electron in the gas in question. Naturally this is only valid provided μ = Const. (see Chapter 9). If it is assumed that the initial velocity of the electrons is zero and that ionization does not take place, it is easy to show that:

$$\boxed{j = \frac{9}{32\pi} \cdot \mu \frac{V_a^2}{d^3}} \quad \text{(CGS ESU)} \tag{10.6}$$

and to find curves analogous to those in Fig. 10.5.

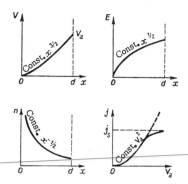

Fig. 10.5. Space charge limited emission at medium or high pressure

The discontinunity in n at $x = 0$ is again due to the hypothesis that $v_0 = 0$.

When j_s is small and V_a is large, curves analogous to those in Fig. 10.6 will be obtained with

$$dV/dx = E = \text{Const.} \quad \text{and} \quad j = j_s$$

whence

$$v = \text{Const.} \quad \text{and} \quad n = \text{Const.}$$

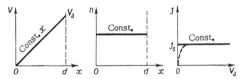

Fig. 10.6. Limitation of the discharge by cathode emission at medium or high pressure

10.1.3 Remarks

(a) The preceding sections demonstrate the extent to which the presence of electric charges modifies the distribution of the field and potential between two electrodes: space charge is a fundamental phenomenon of electric dicharges.

(b) If the anode emits positive charge while the cathode remains inactive, phenomena symmetric with respect to those described above will be observed: the curvature of $V = f(x)$ would be reversed so that it would be concave with respect to the x axis. The curve $j = f(V_a)$ is not modified (Fig. 10.7).

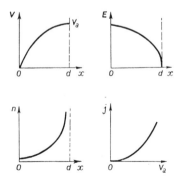

Fig. 10.7. Positive space charge emission characteristics

(c) In the case of a discharge at high pressure, the electric charges are subject to motion due to thermal agitation which is superimposed on their motion due to the electric field. The agitation velocity is a great deal larger than that due to the electric field. To be rigorous, the results of this diffusion from regions of high density to those of low density should be taken into account, since this contributes to the electric current.

(d) In the case of coaxial cylindrical geometry (also in vacuum), the $V^{3/2}$ law remains valid and most of the phenomena have the same form (very important for all discharge tubes).

(e) In all the cases discussed up to now, the discharge currents were eventually limited by the thermionic or photoelectric emission of the electrodes. This leads to current densities lower than 1 A/cm².

It is possible to obtain more intense currents if the gas pressure and the p.d. (potential difference) between the electrodes is such that each charge can ionize a certain number of molecules in its passage. In the following sections, we shall investigate this multiplication phenomenon starting with the case of primary charges produced not at the surface of the electrode but in the gas as secondary charges.

10.2 Production of charges within a gas

The space between the two electrodes can easily be ionized by heating it by means of a flame or irradiating it with X-rays or ultraviolet rays. Let v be the number of ion pairs formed per unit volume and time in the gas under consideration. Let us assume that each pair of ions is made up of a negative electron and a heavy positive ion. If V_a is made to increase progressively, j at first increases linearly with V_a and then tends to a saturation value j_s (see Fig. 10.8).

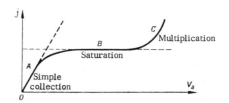

Fig. 10.8. Ionization chamber characteristic

When V_a becomes sufficiently large, j_s begins to increase again, this time very rapidly. We shall investigate the three parts (A, B, C) of this characteristic, which is very important since it represents the behavior of the ionization chambers used in nuclear physics. Besides this, it is the first part of the general characteristic of continuous current discharges in gases.

10.2.1 $V_a = 0$

If no electric field is applied, the ions formed diffuse slowly until they disappear due to recombination or contact with the walls. Let us assume that the pressure and temperature are such that the second possibility is very unlikely.

Then, if n_+ and n_- are the ion densities, equilibrium is quickly established such that

$$\nu = \alpha\, n_+\, n_- = \alpha\, n^2$$

since $n_+ = n_- = n$ at every instant. Hence,

$$n = \sqrt{\nu/\alpha} \tag{10.7}$$

10.2.2 V_a small: collection without multiplication

At every point there is a field $E = V_a/d$ which causes each sort of ion to move towards the electrode of opposite sign with a velocity dependent on its mobility. The total current density in the gas is:

$$j = n\, e(v_+ + v_-) = e\sqrt{\nu/\alpha}\,(\mu_+ + \mu_-)\, E \tag{10.8}$$

Thus, j is indeed proportional to the electric field or p.d. as shown experimentally (Fig. 10.8, region A).

Numerical example: atmospheric pressure; $E = 1\text{V/cm} = 100$ V/m; $e = 1.6 \cdot 10^{-9}$ C; $\nu = 10^{14}$ pairs/sec·m^3; $\alpha = 10^{-6}$ cm^3/sec $= 10^{-12}$ m^3/sec; $\mu \approx 1$ (cm/sec)/V/cm) $\approx 10^{-4}$ m^2/V·sec; whence $j \approx 10^{-8}$ A/m$^2 = 10^{-12}$ A/cm^2.

The current (10.8) could be considered as the sum of an ionic current (μ_+) and an electronic current (μ_-). Now we know (Chapter 9) that $\mu_+ \ll \mu_-$. In other words, the electrons will be "sucked in" by the anode much faster than the positive ions will disappear at the cathode. This is impossible in the steady state since the rate of production of ions is the same as that of electrons. The electrons will therefore collect on the surface of the anode; the resultant electric field will be taken from the initial field V_a/d and will tend to repulse the incident electrons which will decelerate and will form a negative space charge in front of the anode. On the other hand, there will be an excess of positive charge in front of the cathode due to the rapid departure of the electrons in the direction of the anode. As ν increases, the distributions of V, E, and $\rho = (n_+ - n_-)\, e$ pass progressively from the form in Fig. 10.9(a) to the form in 10.9(b).

The field is greater at the cathode than at the anode and this compensates for the smaller mobility of the ions and balances the two components of the total current.

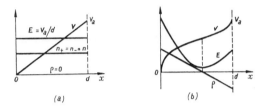

Fig. 10.9. Effect of the space charge in an ionization chamber

At low values of ν, perturbation due to the space charge is negligible and we have approximately

$$j \approx ne\,\mu_-\,E \approx ne\,\mu_-\,V_a/d$$

As V_a progressively increases, j also increases but less and less (region B in Fig. 10.8); it tends to a saturation value which is determined by ν and d only and no longer by V_a. In effect, the velocity acquired by the ions of both signs is such that the law of diffusion is no longer obeyed; recombinations become rarer and rarer, and a state is reached whereby all ions of the same type are captured by the electrode with the opposite sign as fast as they are created. It is obvious that the current cannot increase after this. Let us calculate the limiting value under these conditions.

Fig. 10.10. Calculation of saturation current

Let us consider a pair of ions formed at the instant $t = 0$ at point x between the two electrodes (Fig. 10.10). Let i_+ be the instantaneous current induced in the external circuit by the movement of the positive charge towards the cathode under the action of the field E between time zero and time T.

According to the principle of conservation of energy

$$e \int_x^0 - E \, dx = V_a \int_0^{T_+} i_+ \, dt$$

At the same time, for the electron

$$- e \int_x^d - E \, dx = V_a \int_0^{T_-} i_- \, dt$$

Adding term by term

$$e \, V_a = V_a \int_0^{T_+} (i_+ + i_-) \, dt = V_a \int_0^{T_+} i \, dt$$

since $T_+ > T_-$ and $i_+ + i_- = i =$ total current. The total charge displaced in the external circuit during time T is thus

$$\int_0^{T_+} i \, dt = e$$

and not $2 e$.

If ν pairs are produced per unit time and volume, the current in the external circuit per unit of surface of the electrode will be given by

$$\boxed{j_s = e \, (d \times 1) \, \nu = ed \, \nu} \qquad (10.9)$$

10.2.3 V_a *large: multiplication of charge*

To explain the increase in current density beyond its saturation value (part C of the characteristic 10.8), another phenomenon must be introduced, that of ionization of the gas by the primary electrons. When V_a is greater than or equal to the ionization potential, V_i, of the gas, the electrons produced by the external ionization agent (radiation, heat, etc.) can acquire an energy from the electric field which is sufficient for them in turn to ionize the molecules of the gas. The same will be true for the electrons produced as a result, and so on. This snowball (avalanche) effect produces a rapid increase in the total current.

Mathematical analysis of the phenomenon is complicated because, as we know, the ionization cross section depends on the velocity of the electrons and this varies constantly even for one electron. In practice, all that can be done is to define and measure a macroscropic coefficient α, which represents the mean number of pairs of ions formed by an electron in a path of 1 cm. α is called the first Townsend coefficient.

Let us consider a layer of gas of thickness dx, unit surface in the plane x (Fig. 10.10). $N_0 = v \cdot dx$ primary electrons leave this per unit time. When they arrive at a point $y > x$ in the direction of the abscissa, these electrons are accompanied by all the electrons formed by the avalanche between x and y. Let $N(y)$ be the total number of electrons at y belonging to the N_0 group. In the interval y to $y + dy$, these will give rise to

$$dN = N(y)\, \alpha \, dy$$

electrons. Thus

$$dN/N = \alpha \, dy$$

whence

$$N(y) = N_0 \exp\left[\alpha(y - x)\right]$$
$$N(d) = N_0 \exp\left[\alpha(d - x)\right] = v \exp\left[\alpha(d - x)\right] dx$$

Each layer of gas undergoes the same process. In a steady state, the total number of electrons which reach unit surface of the anode (or positive ions which reach the cathode) in unit time will be:

$$v \int_0^d \exp\left[\alpha(d - x)\right] dx = \frac{v}{\alpha}(e^{\alpha d} - 1)$$

This corresponds to a current

$$\boxed{j = \frac{j_s}{\alpha d}(e^{\alpha d} - 1)} \qquad (10.10)$$

where $j_s = e\, v\, d =$ "primary" current (Eq. 10.9).

Remarks:

1. $j \propto j_s \propto v$ (application to proportional counters).
2. $j \to j_s$ when $\alpha\, d \to 0$.
3. j increases rapidly with $\alpha\, d$; in particular j increases with d (disobeying Ohm's law) (Fig. 10.11).
4. If all electrons come from the cathode $j = j_s \exp(\alpha\, d)$. If the cathode emission is thermal in origin, j_s may reach 1 A/cm^2 and j several amperes (i.e., arc!).
5. Recombination is negligible (E/p large).

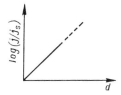

Fig. 10.11. Influence of the distance between the electrodes on the multiplication of charge

The coefficient α depends on E, p and the nature of the gas. It has been shown experimentally that for a specified gas α/p only depends on E/p. (Note that α/p is proportional to the number of electrons formed on average along the mean free path.)

Figure 10.12 represents various experimental results.

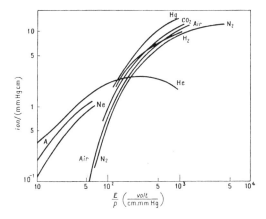

Fig. 10.12. First Townsend coefficient for various gases.
(A. von ENGEL, *Hnd. d. Phys.*, **21**, Springer, 1956)

At low values of E/p, the curves are accurately represented by an equation of the form (Fig. 10.13)

$$\alpha/p = A \exp[- B/(E/p)] \qquad (10.11)$$

The experimental maxima in α/p $(= A)$ are of the order of **10 pairs/mm Hg· cm.**

When the total number of electric charges displaced is large, space charges appear which perturb the electric field and cause α to vary from one point to another in the discharge.

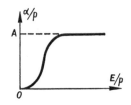

Fig. 10.13. Curve representing
(10.11)

Finally, if E/p is too high, the ions and electrons impinge on the respective electrodes with such energy that they extract new charged particles and these accelerate the avalanche effect once again. This phenomenon will be the subject of the next chapter.

11 the townsend discharge

In the last chapter, we investigated nonselfsustaining discharges which are characterized by the fact that the electric current across the gas disappears when the external ionizing agent ceases to act. The current is proportional to the intensity of the ionization in discharges of this type.

We shall now consider another kind of discharge: the self-sustaining discharges, so called because they can survive the disappearance of the ionizing agent which gave rise to them. All other things being equal, these discharges appear when the p.d. applied to the electrodes exceeds a minimum value. Once this value has been passed, the discharge current no longer depends on the intensity of ionization.

The nature and conditions of setting up a self-sustaining discharge differ widely depending on whether the pressure of the gas is low or high. When the pressure is high, the current transported is intense ($>$ 1 A): a brief spark or continuous arc is produced according to the capacity of the source of p.d. On the other hand, at medium or low pressure the discharge current remains relatively small ($\approx$ several μ A).

The present chapter will deal with the latter type of discharges, which are called Townsend discharges; and we shall then return to arcs and sparks.

11.1 Charge multiplication with secondary effects. Breakdown

Let us return to our ideal experimental apparatus consisting of two plane, parallel, metallic electrodes separated by a distance d. We have seen that, when the p.d. is sufficiently high, the current density exceeds its saturation value j_s while remaining proportional to it (Eq. 10.10). If the p.d. applied to the electrodes then increases again, the coefficient of proportionality increases more rapidly than would be predicted by expression (10.10).

This can be explained by taking into account new processes which we shall now investigate. First, the electrons arriving at the anode cause secondary emission of positive ions which contribute to the electric current.

Besides this, when an electron appears due to ionization of the gas it is accompanied by a positive ion which starts to move towards the cathode. On its way it may further ionization of the gas (β effect). The same ion may hit the cathode with an energy sufficient to eject a secondary electron (γ effect). At the same time photons emitted during ion-electron recombinations and atoms raised to a metastable state after a collision may extract secondary electrons from the cathode (δ and ε effects). Of all these phenomena, the last three, which are localized at the cathode, are the most effective, especially the first of the three.

It has been found that the current density of a discharge depends on the nature of the cathode.

Under these conditions, the coefficient of multiplication is found in the following manner for the (most simple) case of initial ionization only taking place at the cathode.

We know that $e^{\alpha d}$ electrons arrive at the anode for every electron leaving the cathode (Section 10.2.3). Each electron thus gives rise to $e^{\alpha d} - 1$ ion pairs in the course of its path. The corresponding $e^{\alpha d} - 1$ ions in their turn arrive at the cathode and extract from it $\gamma(e^{\alpha d} - 1)$ secondary electrons, γ being the second Townsend coefficient. (Note that all the secondary electrons are attributed to positive ions in this theory.) All the $\gamma(e^{\alpha d} - 1)$ electrons of the 2nd generation undergo the same process as the initial electron, and so on. Thus the flux at the anode due to the single initial electron is

$$e^{\alpha d} + \gamma(e^{\alpha d} - 1) e^{\alpha d} + \gamma^2 (e^{\alpha d} - 1)^2 e^{\alpha d} + \dots$$
$$= e^{\alpha d} \left[1 + \gamma(e^{\alpha d} - 1) + \gamma^2(e^{\alpha d} - 1)^2 + \dots \right]$$
$$= \frac{e^{\alpha d}}{1 - \gamma(e^{\alpha d} - 1)} = m \tag{11.1}$$

where m is the multiplication coefficient of the discharge.

From this it can be seen that, when $\gamma(e^{\alpha d} - 1) \approx 1$, m increases with d a great deal faster than $e^{\alpha d}$ (multiplication without secondary effects; compare Figs. 11.1 and 10.11).

If the initial ionization takes place in the body of the gas and not at the cathode, the multiplication coefficient depends on the abscissa of the point at which the initial electron appears. However, the factor $1-\gamma(e^{\alpha d}-1)$ will still appear in the denominator of the new expression for m, and determines the form of the observed phenomena.

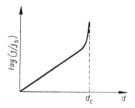

Fig. 11.1. Multiplication of charge with secondary effects

In particular, m becomes infinite when the electric field in the gas reaches a value such that:

$$\boxed{\gamma(e^{\alpha d}-1)=1}\ \text{Townsend criterion} \qquad (11.2)$$

The physical significance of this is that:

1. a single ionization due to some external cause may give rise to a very intense current;

2. this current cannot be infinite but, being no longer determined by the existence of an ionization agent, it is only limited by the internal resistance R_i of the source of p.d. and, of course, by the maximum output available. In other words, the internal dynamic resistance $(\mathrm{d}V/\mathrm{d}I)$ of the discharge is zero (Fig. 11.2).

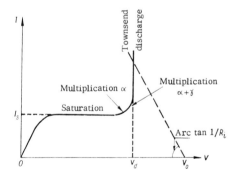

Fig. 11.2. Townsend discharge

Whatever the E.M.F. V_0 of the source, the p.d. at the boundaries of the discharge is equal to V_d; V_d is said to be the disruption or breakdown voltage.

Under these conditions, the p.d. at the boundaries of the electrodes can no longer serve as variable parameter. It has to be replaced by the electric current (or current density); this is why the characteristic diagrams of self-sustaining discharges have I as abscissa and V_a as ordinate.

11.2 Paschen's law

αd can also be written $(\alpha/E)V_d$. If we make $\alpha/E = \eta$, (11.2) has the form $\gamma[\exp (\eta V_d) - 1] = 1$ or

$$V_d = (1/\eta)ln\ (1/\gamma + 1) \approx \text{Const.}/\eta \tag{11.3}$$

Now

$$\eta = \frac{\alpha}{E} = \frac{\alpha}{p} \cdot \frac{p}{E} = F(p/E) = G(pd/V)$$

Finally,

$$\boxed{V_d = f(pd)} \tag{11.4}$$

This is the first part of Paschen's law.

Experimental curves often represent $\eta = \alpha/E$ instead of α or α/p; V_d then varies as the inverse of $\eta = \alpha d/V_d$, which is also (to all intents and purposes) the number of ionizations per electron and per volt applied.

Figures 11.3 and 11.4 represent some experimental results for the breakdown voltage of various gases.

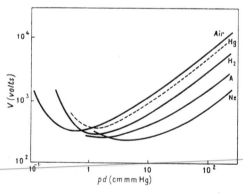

Fig. 11.3. Paschen curves (A. von ENGEL, *Ionized Gases*, Clarendon Press, 1955, p. 172)

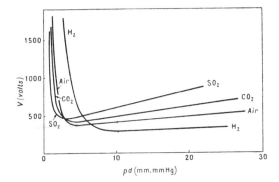

Fig. 11.4. Paschen curves, (M. KNOLL et al., *Tables of Gas Discharges*, Springer, 1935, p. 84)

The curves show a clear minimum (this is the second part of Paschen's law) which can easily be explained as follows.

At low pressures (for a given distance between the electrodes), the mean free paths of electrons are very long and the probability of collisions very small, and the smaller the lower the pressure. At high pressures, on the other hand, the m.f.p.'s are so short that the electrons cannot acquire a large energy between two successive collisions and the less so the higher the pressure. In these two extreme cases, the probability of ionization, hence α and η, are small and V_d large. Between the two, at medium pressures, V_d therefore passes through a minimum.

Note that then:

$d \approx$ some tens of λ

$$\lambda = \frac{1}{n\sigma} = \frac{1}{p \times 3,5 \times 10^{16} \times 10^{-15}} = \frac{1}{35\,p}$$

and $pd \approx 1$.

11.3 Factors determining the minimum Paschen coordinates

For the majority of pure gases, the minimum breakdown voltage, $(V_d)_{min}$, is between 100 and 500 V and corresponds to values of pd in the range 10^{-1} to 10 mm Hg cm. It should be noted that this minimum is very shallow.

11.3.1 Influence of gaseous impurities

If a small quantity of another gas is added to a pure gas, α and η may increase considerably, and V_d will decrease in consequence.

Example: For Ne or A, $(V_d)_{min} \approx 250$ V.

If 1% of argon is added to neon, $(V_d)_{min}$ falls to ≈ 200 V. This can be explained as follows: there is a high probability that Ne atoms will be excited by electrons; in particular, the metastable (long-lived) levels $2S_5$ and $2S_3 (\Delta L = 0; \Delta J = 3$ and 5) can be excited (16.6 V); in returning to the ground level, an atom excited in this way can ionize an atom of A $(V_i = 15.7$ V). This indirect ionization will greatly increase η.

11.3.2 Influence of the cathode

Although γ only appears in the expression for V_d in the form of a logarithm, its influence can be clearly demonstrated by changing the nature of the cathode.

In general, γ has a minimum at medium values of E/p. The increase in γ at low values of E/p is probably due to the influence of metastable atoms and photons incident on the cathode.

The most important feature in this field is that γ is larger in the case of alkaline metals and alkaline earths (small work function) than in the case of other metals (see Fig. 11.5).

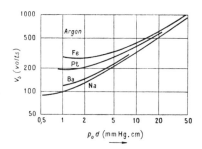

Fig. 11.5. Influence of the material of the cathode on the breakdown voltage (PENNING, *Electric Discharges in Gases*, Dunod, 1957, p. 33)

11.3.3

The following table gives several examples illustrating the above remarks.

Gas	Cathode	$(V_d)_{min}$ (volts)	$(pd)_{min}$ (mmHg-cm)
He.........	Fe	150	2.5
Ne.........	Fe	244	3
Air.........	Fe	330	0.57
A	Fe	265	1.5
N_2.........	Fe	275	0.75
O_2.........	Fe	450	0.7
Na.........	Fe	335	0.04
Hg.........	Fe	520	2
Hg.........	W	425	1.8
Hg.........	Hg	330	—
H_2.........	Pt	295	1.25

11.4 Perturbation effects

11.4.1 Attachment of electrons

In the case of electronegative gases, the tendency of electrons to attach themselves to molecules or atoms should be taken into account. This occurs in oxygen, the halogens and compounds of halogens.

Since the mobility and ionizing power of negative ions are a great deal smaller than those of electrons, this phenomenon of attachment considerably reduces the discharge current.

Let a be the number of attachments of an electron to a molecule per unit length of the electron path in the direction of the field. $a \ll 1/\lambda$ should be considered as a probability of attachment per unit length.

For every n_e electrons crossing the plane of the abscissa x, there are $\alpha n_e \, dx$ ionizations and $a n_e \, dx$ attachments between x and $x + d$ (Fig. 11.6).

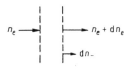

$$n_e \longrightarrow \qquad \longrightarrow n_e + dn_e$$
$$\longrightarrow dn_-$$

Fig. 11.6

In this way, when the initial group of n_e electrons arrives at $x + dx$, it has been increased by dn_e electrons and dn_- negative ions, where

$$dn_e = (\alpha - a) \, n_e \, dx$$

I

and

$$dn_- = an_e\, dx$$

For every n_0 electrons leaving the cathode there are

$$n_e = n_0 \exp[(\alpha - a)\, d] \text{ electrons}$$

and

$$n_- = \frac{n_0 a}{\alpha - a} \left[\exp[(\alpha - a)\, d] - 1\right] \text{ negative ions}$$

at the anode.

The coefficient of multiplication is thus:

$$m = \frac{n_e + n_-}{n_0} = \frac{1}{\alpha - a} \left[\alpha \exp[(\alpha - a)\, d] - a\right] \tag{11.5}$$

if there are no secondary effects at the cathode $(\gamma = 0)$.

It can be seen that if $\alpha \overset{\sim}{\lesssim} a$, $m \ll \exp(\alpha d)$.

The same conclusion is valid if $\gamma \neq 0$.

Figure 11.7 gives some experimental results for the coefficient a.

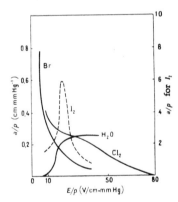

Fig. 11.7. Coefficient of attachment of electrons in various gases. (F. PREVOT, in "Theory and Technique of Accelerators," Vol. 3, INSTN (1959), p. 192)

11.4.2 Effects of space charge

If the current density is small enough ($< 1 \ \mu A/cm^2$, for example), the field E is uniform between two plane electrodes. Above this value, with intense currents, positive charges begin to accumulate in the neighborhood of the anode thus deforming the potential distribution (cf. Fig. 10.9b); α then varies as a function of x, and the condition 11.2 defining V_d becomes:

$$\gamma \left[\exp \left(\int_0^d \alpha \, dx - 1 \right) \right] = 1$$

In this case this equation leads to values of V_d which are smaller than those corresponding to the absence of space charge. The characteristic of the discharge should curve in as at D in Fig. 11.8.

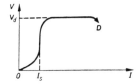

Fig. 11.8. Effect of space charge
on the Townsend discharge

11.4.3 Nature of electrodes

If the electrodes are not plane, the electric field is no longer uniform. Depending on whether the field is magnified or diminished in the vicinity of the cathode, the multiplication factor increases or decreases and the breakdown voltage rises or falls. If the polarity of the electrodes is changed, the phenomena no longer have the same form: voltage, current, form of the beam of electric charge, etc. This is again due to the fact that the cathode plays the largest part in secondary effects.

11.5 Formative time lag

For the Townsend discharge to begin, a first electron must appear in the gas, and then the ions created in the path of this electron must arrive at the cathode and liberate secondary electrons.

The time between the application of the p.d. to the boundaries of the electrodes and the appearance of the first electron essentially depends on the circumstances: the mean of this time is called the statistical time lag; it depends on the intensity of ambient, natural (cosmic, light, etc.) or artificial (radioactive source) radiation.

The time between the appearance of the first electron and the establishment of a steady state is called the formative time. It is of the order of 10^{-4} or 10^{-5} **sec.**

11.6 Form of discharge

The Townsend discharge is not very luminous as the current is not very intense. This is the reason why it is sometimes called a dark discharge. The luminosity is more or less uniform throughout the whole of the space between the electrodes.

12 the glow discharge

Figure 12.1 represents the general nature of the V-I character-istics of gaseous discharges for pressures in the range 0.1 to 10 mm Hg.

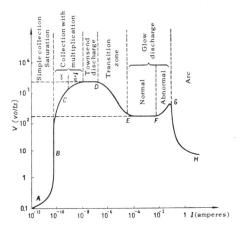

Fig. 12.1. Schematic characteristic for a gaseous discharge

This shows the types of discharge already investigated in Chapter 9 (A, B, C) and in Chapter 10 (C–D, Townsend discharge) as well as the luminous discharge region to be discussed in the present chapter.

12.1 Transition zone and stability of states

The electric circuit used to investigate the *V-I* characteristic can have a large influence on the results.

The normal circuit is shown by the sketch in Fig. **12.2.** *E* or *R* is varied and *V* and *I* observed.

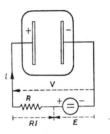

Fig. 12.2. Plotting a characteristic

For a set of values of E and R for the E.M.F. of the generator G and the resistance drop (which includes the internal resistance of the generator), V and I are given by the system of equations

$$(a)\ V = E - RI \qquad (b)\ V = f(I) \qquad (12.1)$$

where $f(I)$ is the characteristic of the discharge (Fig. 12.1).

In the diagram in Fig. 12.3, Eq. (12.1a) is represented by the straight line D (the load line) and Eq. (12.1b) by the curve C.

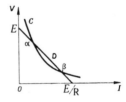

Fig. 12.3. α—unstable state; β—stable state

The coordinates of the points of intersection of C and D are solutions to the system of Eqs. (12.1). Each of these points represents a state of equilibrium.

For a single E, R combination, there can be a number of these points but they do not all correspond to stable states.

In the vicinity of one of these points, Eq. (12.1b) can be written (expansion limited to the first order)

$$V = V_0 + (dV/dI)_0 \, \Delta I = V_0 + \rho_0 \Delta I$$

ρ_0 = dynamic resistance at the point in question.

If, for some reason, the current in the discharge varies by ΔI with respect to its equilibrium value, an E.M.F. of

$$\Delta e = E - V - RI = -(\rho_0 + R) \, \Delta I$$

taken as positive in a clockwise direction (Fig. 12.1) appears in the circuit.

It is clear that:

—if $\rho_0 + R > 0$, Δe is in the opposite direction to ΔI and tends to counteract the perturbation; cf. point β, stable equilibrium;

—if $\rho_0 + R < 0$, Δe is in the same direction as ΔI and tends to reinforce the perturbation; unstable equilibrium, cf. point α. The point of action moves rapidly in the direction of a point of type β.

Thus, to plot the whole characteristic without any difficulty, it would be best to use a generator with an infinite internal resistance, that is to say, an adjustable direct current generator. In this case the load line is parallel to the V axis. If this is not possible, a generator with a constant high E.M.F. can be used in series with a large resistance.

All these remarks apply to the transition zone DE (Fig. 12.1) characterized by a dynamic resistance $\rho < o$. An inductance or capacity or both in the circuit may produce sinusoidal or relaxation oscillations under these conditions. Since these reactive elements are always present, if only in a parasitic form, the discharge in this zone is often perturbed by oscillations which may have a very large amplitude.

12.2 The glow discharge

12.2.1 Form of discharge

When the current in a Townsend discharge increases, the voltage between the electrodes diminishes (Fig. 12.1) and a new type of discharge is eventually established. This is the glow discharge, characterized by the appearance of several diffuse luminous zones and by a constant p.d. between the electrodes.

As usual, experiments are carried out with a sealed cylindrical glass tube containing two plane parallel electrodes, one at each end of the tube. To simplify the theoretical analysis of the phenomena, it is assumed that the electrodes are infinite.

Figure 12.4 represents the different regions which can be observed between these electrodes.

The color of the light emitted varies with the gas and the region under investigation. Thus in air the negative glow is bluish while the positive column is pink (see *Handbuch der Physik*, **XXII**, p. 58).

The relative size of the various zones varies with the pressure and the distance between the electrodes.

As the pressure decreases, the negative glow and the Faraday dark space expand at the expense of the positive column which may disappear completely. At the same time, if the distance between the electrodes decreases, the positive column diminishes in the same ratio without the size of the other zones varying at all. If the cathode is displaced, all zones up to the Faraday dark zone are

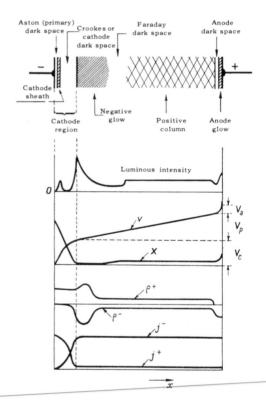

Fig. 12.4. Normal glow discharge. The shaded areas are luminous. (A. von ENGEL, *Ionized Gases*, Clarendon Press, 1957, p. 191)

displaced with it. Finally, if the electrodes are mounted in a large spherical enclosure instead of a tube, no positive column can be observed.

These facts show that, on the one hand, the electrons have essentially linear trajectories in the vicinity of the cathode, and, on the other hand, that the positive column is not characteristic of the discharge as are the clear and dark zones in the neighborhood of the cathode.

The potential V does not vary linearly as a function of the distance from one of the electrodes. This is due to space charge.

The p.d. V at the boundaries of the discharge tube is made up of

V_c = cathode fall in potential,
V_p = fall over positive column,
V_a = anode fall in potential.

$$V_n = V_c + V_p + V_a$$

It is worth noting that $V_c \gg V_p + V_a$. What is more, under certain conditions, $V_a = 0$. Otherwise $V_a \approx$ first ionization potential of the gas.

In the positive column, the electric field is constant and not very intense: a few volts per centimeter.

Thus in general

$$V_n \approx V_c$$

V_c is characteristic of the combination of gas and cathode material in question; it varies little with pressure, distance between the electrodes and discharge current as long as the latter does not exceed a certain limiting value I_F (Fig. 12.5).

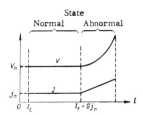

Fig. 12.5

The electric charge density is only large in the cathode region. This can easily be explained by realizing that all the slow, positive ions flow towards the cathode which, in addition, emits a large quantity of electrons.

The resultant space charge is practically zero over the whole length of the tube: the gas is in the form of a plasma. But the "density of the plasma" $(\rho = \rho_+ = |\rho_-|)$ in the negative column is 10 to 100 times greater than that of the positive column.

If the resultant current density $j = j_+ + j_-$ is the same over the whole length of the tube (according to the principle of conservation of charge, in a steady state), it is far from being the same for its components $j_+ = \rho_+ v_+$ and $j_- = \rho_- v_-$. In the positive column, $\rho_- = \rho_+$, but since the mobility of the electrons is much greater, $j_- \gg j_+$. At the anode, $j_+ = 0$. In the vicinity of the cathode, $\rho_+ \gg \rho_-$; this more than compensates for the slowness of the ions and $j_+ \gg j_-$. On the cathode: $j_- = 0$.

12.2.2 Cathode region

This is the name given to the region of length d stretching from the surface of the cathode to the negative glow (not inclusive). It corresponds to the cathode fall in potential V_c, that is to say, more or less V_n.

The theory relating to phenomena connected with the cathode is based on the following hypotheses:

(a) All the cathode electrons are emitted under the effect of ion bombardment (2nd Townsend coefficient).

(b) The electric field in the vicinity of the cathode decreases linearly as a function of distance x (an experimental fact).

(c) The condition for the maintenance of the discharge is

$$\gamma \left[\exp \left(\int_0^d \alpha \, dx \right) - 1 \right] = 1$$

that is to say, the same as in the case of the Townsend discharge but applied to the interval o-d corresponding to the cathode fall in potential. Thus it is assumed that all the ions appear in the cathode region which behaves like a Townsend discharge tube.

12.2.2.1 *Normal state.* These hypotheses lead to the following results for a normal glow discharge (region E, F of Fig. 12.1).

$$\boxed{\begin{aligned} V_{cn} &= C_1 \ln(1 + 1/\gamma) \\ \frac{j_n}{p^2} &= C_2 \left(\frac{1 + \gamma}{\ln(1 + 1/\gamma)} \right) \\ p \cdot d_n &= C_3 \ln(1 + 1/\gamma) \end{aligned}}$$ (12.2)

In these formulas, C_1, C_2 and C_3 are constants which only depend on the gas used, while γ depends, as is well known on the combination of gas and material of the cathode. Hence:

1. V_{cn} is independent of p,
2. j_n is proportional to p^2 (to p for cylindrical electrodes). $j_n \gg I/S$ where S is the surface area of the electrodes,
3. d_n is proportional to p^{-1}.

These results have been fairly well verified by experiment, bearing in mind the difficulties of measurement and the great importance of impurities, even in very small quantities.

Table 12.1 gives the values of V_{cn}, j_n/p^2 and pd_n for various combinations of gas and cathode material.

Table 12.1. Cathode fall in potential V_{cn}; current density j; length of cathode region d, for various gases and cathodes (according to von Engel)

Cathode \ Gas	He	Ne	A	H_2	N_2	Air	Hg	O_2	
Cu	177	220	130	214	208	375	450		V_{cn}(volts)
Zn	143		119	184	216	280		354	
Hg	143			337	226		340		
Al	140	120	100	170	180	230	245	310	
Fe	150	150	165	250	215	270	300	290	
Ni	160	140	130	210	200	226	275		
Pt	165	152	130	276	216	277		364	
K.	60	68	64	94	170	180			
Cu				64		240	15		j_n (10^{-6} A/cm^2) for
Au				110		570			1 mm Hg or j_n/p^2
Mg	3	5	20						
Al				90		330	4		
Fe/Ni.	2	6	160	72	400		8		
Pt	5	18	150	90	380	550			
Cu				0.8		0.23	0.6		d_n (cm) for 1 mm Hg
Mg	1.45			0.61	0.35			0.25	or pd_n
Hg				0.9					
Al	1.32	1.64	0.29	0.72	0.31	0.25	0.33	0.24	
Fe	1.3	0.72	0.33	0.9	0.42	0.52	0.34	0.31	

From these it can be seen that:

1. V_{cn} is generally smaller the smaller the work function of the cathode and ionization potential of the gas.

Thus: V_{cn} = 94 V for K in H_2
V_{cn} = 220 V for Cu in N_r
V_c is smaller for rare gases than for molecular gases.

2. $V_{cn} \leqslant$ the Paschen breakdown potential.
3. j_n/p^2 is low for Hg and rare gases (except A) and high for molecular gases.
4. d_n represents 50 to 100 m.f.p.

12.2.2.2 Abnormal state. The values of V_c, j and d given by the Eqs. (12.2) for a normal discharge correspond to a minimum in V_c and j/p^2 and to a maximum in pd. They are valid as long as the discharge does not cover the whole of the cathode, that is to say, the region E, F of the characteristic in Fig. 12.1.

Beyond this point, V_c and j increase as d diminishes as in Figs. 12.5 and 12.6.

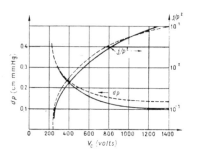

Fig. 12.6. Abnormal state of glow discharge in nitrogen with an ion cathode (region F G of the characteristic illustrated in Fig. 12.1). (A. GUNTHERSCHULZE, Z. Phys. 59, 433, 1930)

This development is explained by the fact that, for a particular cathode surface, I cannot exceed $I_F = j_n S$ unless $j > j_n$. But then the charge density increases in the vicinity of the cathode; hence, the field is greater when V is larger and d is smaller.

12.2.2.3 Form of the cathode region. In the Aston dark space, the electrons coming from the cathode do not have enough energy to ionize or to excite the atoms of the gas. On the other hand, the ions moving towards the cathode already have a velocity such that the probability of a radiative recombination is small. Finally, the excited ions have already had time to return to their ground level. As a result of these facts, this region does not emit any radiation.

The cathode sheath will appear at the point where ions excited by electrons return to their ground level.

In Crookes dark space the gas is ionized by the electrons which have not lost any energy in exciting the atoms of the cathode sheath, but which, on the other hand, have been accelerated by the electric field. Multiplication of the charges results, but the electrons liberated in this way do not have enough energy to excite the gas, while the energy of the electrons which gave rise to them is still too great. Due to this lack of excitation or recombination, this region emits little light.

12.2.3 The negative glow

In this region, the large number of secondary electrons liberated in the dark space begin to excite the ambient gas atoms. There is therefore an abundant emission of light. But the electric field decreases and with it the energy of the electrons and the intensity of the light emitted. Since the density of ions is great in this region, there are a large number of recombinations. Nevertheless, the recombination radiation is not very intense.

12.2.4 Faraday dark space

In this region, the electrons which lost their energy in the region of negative glow cannot excite or ionize the atoms of the gas. What is more, the field here is so small that they cannot regain much energy.

The small amount of light which this region does emit is due to the excitation of neutral atoms by the metastable atoms present and by photons from the luminous regions.

The electric current in this zone, as in the positive column, is essentially a current due to the diffusion of the charged particles. The directional component of their velocity is much smaller than the component of thermal agitation. This is the inverse situation to that of the cathode region.

12.2.5 Positive column

The positive column fills the whole of the part of the discharge tube from the Faraday dark space to the anode.

It is not characteristic of the luminous discharge:

(a) on the one hand, it is absent if the distance between the electrodes is too small;

(b) on the other hand, ionized volumes with the same characteristics as the positive column can be observed in other types of discharge, for example, arcs. In fact, the positive column is an example of a plasma, and, for this reason, its effect is beyond the scope of classical discharges.

However, it is natural to discuss it at this point since it fills the largest part of luminous discharge tubes (e.g., commercial neon signs).

Remember that we are only dealing with continuous current discharges.

12.2.5.1 Form of positive column. The positive column is the most luminous part of the tube after the negative glow. It may be homogeneous or striated.

These striations only appear under certain conditions of pressure, geometry and current and for certain gases. They may be fixed or move with a longitudinal velocity in the direction of the cathode. Sometimes this motion is so rapid that the region appears homogeneous.

The positive column emits an arc line spectrum. That is to say, the excitation energy involved is small; the electrons are not very fast. As in the Faraday dark space, their displacement velocity is smaller than their velocity due to thermal agitation.

12.2.5.2 Other characteristics. The electrons are slow because of the fact that the electric field E is very small.

Besides this, the field is practically constant:

$$dE/dx = d^2V/dx^2 = 0$$

But this means that (according to Poisson's equation)

$$\rho = \rho_+ - \rho_- = 0 \text{ or } n_+ = n_-$$

This is the definition of a plasma.

The charge density, n_+ or n_-, is of the order of magnitude of 10^{10} cm^{-3} at a pressure of the order of **1 mm Hg**. This gives a degree of ionization of only $10^{10}/3.6 \times 10^{16} \approx 10^{-6}$.

Inelastic collisions only absorb part of the electric energy supplied by the external circuit. The rest is used to heat the gas and the walls of the tube. The energy distribution between these various processes depends on the pressure, the current and the geometry of the tube. In any case, the total power consumption is small—of the order of 1 watt/m at a diameter of 1 cm (an advantage of neon lights).

The temperature of the gas and of the positive ions remains close to the ambient temperature while that of the electrons is several tens of thousands of degrees.

Note: For the same tube, the distribution of potential depends little on the current as long as it does not exceed the limit of the luminous discharge.

12.2.5.3 Theory of the homogeneous positive column at low pressure (0.1 to 10 mm Hg). This theory is based on the following premises:

(*a*) At every point, the macroscopic charge density is zero: $n_- = n_+ = n$.

This is not to say that the mean velocities of thermal agitation of the positive ions and the electrons are the same.

(*b*) Charged particles are lost to the lateral walls and are neutralized by recombination.

(c) Recombination in volume is negligible (T_e high and n small).

(d) Ionization is simple and not cumulative.

(e) There are no negative ions other than the electrons.

(f) The end effects are negligible except for the entry and exit of macroscopic electron and ion currents (in reverse directions).

(g) The radius of the column is large in comparison with the m.f.p. of the electrons.

(h) The density n of ions and electrons becomes zero at the walls.

(i) The lateral walls are assumed to be made of insulating material (glass, for example).

These premises show the importance of the walls in the case of the positive column while they play no part at all in the cathode region of the discharge.

Distribution of electric charges

Neglecting end effects, the distribution has to be investigated only as a function of the distance along the axis (Fig. 12.7).

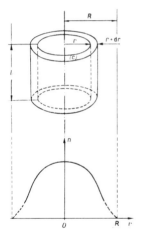

Fig. 12.7. Radial distribution of electric charge. $n(r) = n_+(r) = n_-(r)$; R = radius of discharge tube

We shall consider the most common case, that of a discharge tube with a circular cross section of radius R. The charges diffuse from the axis towards the walls where they recombine.

Since the charge density is assumed to be negligible, this diffusion can only be ambipolar (cf. Chapter 8).

Remember that, in the case where the temperature, and consequently the mobility, of the electrons is a great deal higher than that of the ions, the ambipolar coefficient of diffusion

$$D_a = \frac{D_- \mu_+ + D_+ \mu_-}{\mu_+ + \mu_-}$$

is written

$$D_a = kT_e \mu_+ / e$$

by taking account of the relation $\mu/D = e/kT$.

Having said this, let us take a cylindrical element (C) coaxial to the tube R. The number of ions or electrons entering (C) by its internal face is:

$$- 2\pi r l D_a (dn/dr)_r$$

The number of these leaving the external face is:

$$- 2\pi (r + dr)\, l D_a \left(\frac{dn}{dr}\right)_{r+dr} = - 2\pi l D_a \left[r \frac{dn}{dr} + r \frac{d^2 n}{dr^2}\, dr + \frac{dn}{dr}\, dr \right]$$

The net charge carried in by diffusion is therefore:

$$dv_d = + 2\pi r l D_a \left[\frac{d^2 n}{dr^2} + \frac{1}{r}\frac{dn}{dr} \right]$$

If q is the mean number of ion pairs created per unit time and volume by an electron, the amount of charge due to ionization in the cylinder (C) is:

$$dv_i = 2\pi r l\, dr \cdot nq$$

In equilibrium $dv_d + dv_i = 0$, that is to say:

$$\frac{d^2 n}{dr^2} + \frac{1}{r}\frac{dn}{dr} + \frac{q}{D_a} n = 0$$

This is a Bessel equation of zero order, the solution to which is

$$n(r) = n_0 J_0(\sqrt{q/D_a}\, r)$$

where J_0 is a Bessel function of zero order, the first zero in which occurs when the argument has a value of 2.4.

Since $n(R) = 0$,

$$\boxed{\sqrt{q/D_a}\, R = 2.4} \qquad (12.3)$$

and

$$n(r) = n_0 J_0(2.4\, r/R)$$

(12.4)

n_0 is determined by the experimental conditions.

This relation, which is represented in Fig. 12.7, is well substantiated by experiment (Langmuir probes).

Thus for Ne with $R = 2$ cm, $p = 5$ mm Hg, $I = 50$ mA, $n_0 \approx 10^{11}$ cm^{-3}.

It can easily be shown that in the case of a discharge enclosed between plane, parallel walls the distribution is sinusoidal.

Electron temperature

q and D_a depend, among other things, on the temperature T_e. From the relation $R\sqrt{q/D_a} = 2.4$ it is therefore possible to find T_e as a function of the other parameters of the discharge: radius R, pressure p and the nature of the gas.

$D_a = \mu_+ kT_e/e$, as already mentioned above.

As to q, its value is calculated by supposing that the velocity distribution is Maxwellian

$$(dn)_{(v, v+dv)} = 4\pi n (m/2\pi kT_e)^{3/2}\, v^2\, \exp(-\tfrac{1}{2} mv^2/kT_e)\, dv$$

This is justified by measurements and results which illustrate the fact that the electric field in the positive column is too small to perturb the thermodynamic equilibrium to any extent. Under these conditions, if $N =$ density of neutral molecules and $\sigma_i =$ effective cross section for ionization by the electrons,

$$q = \frac{1}{n} \int_0^\infty N v \sigma_i(v) \cdot dn \;\; \approx A p V_i^{3/2} e^{-x}/\sqrt{x},$$

where:

A = constant dependent on the gas used
p = pressure
V_i = ionization potential of the gas
x = $(eV_i)/kT_e$

Finally, substituting $R\sqrt{q/D_a} = 2.4$:

$$e^x/\sqrt{x} = 1.2 \times 10^7 C^2 (pR)^2$$

(12.5)

p is mm Hg, R is cm.

The constant C is given approximately for various gases in the table below.

Figure 12.8 represents the relation between T_e/V_i and CRp.

K

Table 12.2

Gas	He	Ne	A	Hg	N$_2$	H$_2$
C	$4 \cdot 10^{-3}$	$6 \cdot 10^{-3}$	$4 \cdot 10^{-2}$	$7 \cdot 10^{-2}$	$4 \cdot 10^{-2}$	10^{-2}

It should be noted that T_e depends only on pR. Thus for $R = 2$ cm and $p = 5$ mm Hg, for neon, $T_e \approx 21{,}000\,°K$ independent of the distance r from the axis. These results are well substantiated by experiment (Langmuir probes), except for vapors where the process of cumulative excitation is possible.

The form of the curve in Fig. 12.8 is explained by the fact that the loss of charge due to diffusion increases as the radius of the tube diminishes. To conserve the same current, $S\,j_n$ (see Section 12.2.2), the ionization power would have to increase which entails a rise in temperature (q rises more rapidly than D_a).

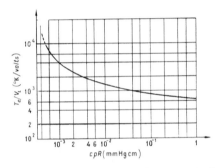

Fig. 12.8. Temperature of the electrons in the positive column. (A. von ENGEL, *Ionized gases*, Clarendon Press, 1955, p. 215)

With higher currents, the heating may be such that the pressure p rises sharply at the axis. Theoretical determination of T_e should take this into account.

The temperature T_i of the ions rises little above that of the neutral particles and the ambient temperature (due to the approximate equality of their masses).

Axial electric field

The electric conductivity of the positive column is not infinite and the current can only be maintained there under the action of an electric field.

For a given current density, the axial field should increase by the same amount as the losses due to diffusion rise. More exactly, the losses in longitudinal energy of the electrons due to collisions with neutral molecules should be compensated by the gain in energy due to the electric field:

$$eEv_d = \varepsilon \left(\frac{mc^2}{2}\right)\left(\frac{C}{\lambda_e}\right) = \varepsilon k T_e \frac{C}{\lambda_e}$$

v_d = drift velocity; C = velocity of thermal agitation; ε = fraction of energy lost due to collision; but $v_d/C \approx \sqrt{\varepsilon}$, hence

$$T_e = \frac{E\lambda_e}{\sqrt{\varepsilon}}\left(\frac{e}{k}\right) \sim \frac{E}{p}$$

Thus from the energy balance it follows that, overall

$$\boxed{T_e \sim E/p} \tag{12.6}$$

The curves representing E/p as a function of pR will have the same form as those for T_e (Fig. 12.9).

Note:

(a) E/p depends very little on the current.

(b) E/p is a great deal larger for molecular gases than for rare gases because the losses due to inelastic collisions are greater for the former.

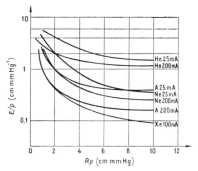

Fig. 12.9. Longitudinal electric field in the positive column. (A. LOMPE and R. SEELIGER, *Ann. Phys.*, **15**, 300, 1932; V. ELENBASS, *Z. Phys.*, **78**, 603, 1932)

Radial electric field

This field results from the ambipolar nature of the radial diffusion. The electrons have a tendency to move more quickly but they are held back by the field E_r due to the positive ions which are following them.

As in Chapter 8:

$$E_r = -\frac{dV}{dr} = \frac{1}{n}\frac{dn}{dr}\frac{D_+ - D_-}{\mu_+ + \mu_-} \approx -\frac{1}{n}\frac{dn}{dr}\frac{D_-}{\mu_-} \approx -\frac{1}{n}\frac{dn}{dr}\frac{kT_e}{e}$$

Now $dn/dr < 0$; so that $E_r > 0$, that is to say, in the direction of the walls as would have been expected (Fig. 12.10).

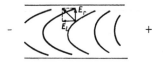

Fig. 12.10. Equipotentials in the positive column

Integrating, we find the potential to be:

$$\begin{aligned} V(r) - V(0) &= -\frac{kT_e}{e}\ln\frac{n_0}{n(r)} \\ &= -\frac{kT_e}{e}\ln\left[\frac{1}{J_0(2.4\,r/R)}\right] \end{aligned} \tag{12.7}$$

Thus $V(r) \leqslant V(0)$ always. But the relations above show that $V(r) \to -\infty$ when $r \to R$, since then $n(r) \to 0$. This is naturally impossible. In fact, these relations are no longer valid in the vicinity of the walls because of their negative charge. If the relation $n_+ = n_-$ were conserved even at the walls, with a Maxwellian velocity distribution the walls would receive a number of electrons $n_-v_-/4$ greater than the number $n_+v_+/4$ of ions per unit time and surface area since $v_- \gg v_+$. This cannot happen except during a short transitory period until the negative charge accumulated on the walls repulses the electrons and attracts the ions sufficiently to establish equal fluxes of each (as in ambipolar diffusion). A Debye sheath is then formed close to the walls, the density of electrons in this sheath being practically zero while the positive ions accumulate. This is true for any insulating wall in contact with a plasma.

In this case the walls are raised to a negative potential with respect to the adjacent plasma:

$$V_D = -\frac{kT_e}{2e}\ln\left(\frac{T_e}{T_i}\frac{m_+}{m_-}\right) \tag{12.8}$$

with $|V_D| \sim 10$ to 20 V.

The diffusion laws in the Debye sheath are different from those for the positive column and it is this which allows the transition from the column to the walls.

The thickness of the Debye sheath is

$$\lambda_D \approx 10^3 \sqrt{T_e/n} \qquad (12.9)$$

with λ_D in cm; T_e in eV; n in cm^{-3}.

If n is very small (for example, at very low pressures), λ_D can be greater than R (i.e., the positive column cannot exist).

12.2.6 Anode region

As long as the anode does not emit any ions it plays a secondary role as a collector of electrons. The discharge does not depend to any extent on its form or its position.

In general, there is a negative space charge in the neighborhood of the anode, accompanied by the anode fall in potential which is of the order of magnitude of the ionization potential, V_i, of the gas. It is in fact in this region that the ions which traverse the positive column are created. Because of the increased probability of excitation, the luminosity increases slightly giving rise to the positive glow.

However, when the surface of the anode is very large, the number of electrons collected by it due to their thermal agitation is so great that the electric field is reversed: there is a positive space charge and a negative anode fall in potential the magnitude of which depends on the surface of the anode.

The anode is heated by the discharge by the following processes:

(a) under the impact of the electrons created in the positive column and possibly accelerated by the anode fall in potential V_a;

(b) due to the liberation of energy during recombinations of ions and electrons on its surface.

If Φ_a is the exit potential at the anode, the total power supplied to it will be:
$$P_a = I(V_a + \Phi_a)$$

12.2.7 Influence of various parameters

(These are close to the values corresponding to the normal discharge, EF in Fig. 12.1.)

12.2.7.1 *Current*. At low currents (region DE of Fig. 12.1), if the current density remains the same, the cross-sectional area of the discharge decreases; the loss of radial charge makes itself felt and should be compensated by a rise in the probability of ionization, which is defrayed by an increase in the cathode drop. This is a subnormal discharge.

In the region of normal discharge (interval EF), the rise in current is accompanied by an increase in the diameter of the discharge, j_n = Const. depending on the gas and the pressure. In the region of abnormal discharge (interval FG), j rises with I, the cathode and the gas becoming more and more heated—not far off an arc.

12.2.7.2 Pressure.

When the pressure increases, the negative zones are compressed in the direction of the cathode, while the positive column expands longitudinally; j increases with p^2. Beyond 100 mm Hg, the positive column contracts radially, the cathode heats up and an arc is again not far off. It is possible to operate a glow discharge even at very high pressure.

When very low pressures are approached, the losses due to diffusion increase and should be compensated by a rise in the cathode fall in potential; all the zones merge one by one with the anode. This is termed a constricted discharge (cf. canal ray discharges).

12.2.7.3 Distance between the electrodes (D).

As this diminishes, the positive column, then the Faraday space and the negative glow become shorter and shorter and successively disappear without the p.d. or the form of the other zones changing much. When the negative flow has disappeared, the p.d. increases rapidly when D diminishes (thwarted or obstructed discharge).

12.2.7.4 Material of the cathode.

The form of the discharge depends little on this. Conversely, the p.d. is considerably reduced in the case of alkaline metals or alkaline earths (small work function). With certain oxide cathodes it is even possible to make the cathode and anode falls in potential disappear.

12.2.7.5 Geometry.

Certain geometries are particularly favorable to ionization and, as a result, give charge densities and current densities which are much higher than others (e.g., perforated cathodes, Penning grid).

The corona discharge or corona effect is obtained with points or wires of small diameter (i.e., with intense electric fields).

12.2.7.6 The gas.

The influence of the gas on the discharge is chiefly on the wavelength of the radiation emitted.

13 the electric arc

Figure 12.1 shows that if the current of a luminous discharge exceeds a certain limit (G), the p.d. between the electrodes diminishes rapidly; the discharge is said to have become an arc.

13.1 Definition

An arc is characterized by the following essential properties:

1. The current density is very high; it may reach several tens of thousands of amperes per cm^2 on the electrodes. In general, it is not so high along the length of the discharge proper, the area of the central cross section of which increases with distance from the electrodes. Even here the current density is $\geqslant 1 \ A/cm^2$.

2. The greater part of the discharge current close to the cathode is carried by the electrons emerging from the latter and not by the ions resulting from the ionization of the gas (cf. luminous discharge, Fig. 12.4).

3. The p.d. between the electrodes is distinctly smaller than for other discharges (in general, some tens of volts).

This definition applies to a very large number of discharges which may differ greatly from one another and which are generally very little understood despite the fact that they are often used.

13.2 Classifications

In the discharges which we have already studied, the emission of electrons by the cathode was a secondary emission due to the impact of ions. In the arc, this is no longer true; other processes must be involved to give rise to the enormous current density mentioned above.

A distinction is made between:

(a) thermionic arcs where the cathode emission is thermal in origin. The cathodes should be of refractory material (C, W, Ta, Mo, etc.);

(b) arcs with field emission where the electrons are extracted from the cathode by the action of a very high field. This field may be due either to a positive space charge in the immediate neighborhood of the cathode or to the existence of an electrically insulating layer on the surface of the latter, this layer being charged by ions and thus raised to a very high positive potential. This type of emission should prevail in the case of so-called metallic arcs where the material of the cathode is not refractory: for example, various interrupters of Cu, Ag, Au, and rectifiers with liquid mercury cathodes (cathode temperature ~ some hundreds of °C). It is possible for the two types of emission to exist simultaneously in certain types of arc.

Among thermionic arcs, which are the more common, a distinction is made between self-sustaining arcs and nonselfsustaining arcs, depending on whether the high temperature of the cathode is maintained by the impact of the accelerated ions or by an external means of heating.

Arcs may be operated at low pressure (10^{-2} mm Hg) or high pressure (several atmospheres), the demarcation line being between 0.1 and 1 atm. This distinction is justified by the sharp change in the properties of the discharge in passing this limit.

The distance between the electrodes may vary from a few microns to several meters and the voltage applied to them may be continuous or alternating.

We shall confine ourselves to a study of long, self-sustaining, thermionic arcs with continuous current.

13.3 Striking an arc

13.3.1 Transition from glow dicharge to arc

We have seen (Section 12.2.2.2) that, in the abnormal state of a glow discharge, an increase in the total current I is necessarily accompanied by a rise in the current density j. At the same time, the thickness of the cathode region diminishes and, as a consequence, the ions lose less energy in collisions. As a result, the energy supplied to the cathode by the impact of ions increases and its temperature rises. Beyond point G of the characteristic in Fig. 12.1, the thermionic emission of the cathode becomes significant. The emitted electrons ionize the gas in front of the cathode, hence supplying additional heat to the latter.

When the thermionic current $I_t > I$, an electron space charge is formed in front of the cathode which locally cancels the electric field. This explains the drop in V in the region GH of the characteristic (Figs. 12.1 and 13.1).

The conditions for this method of striking are the same as those for a luminous discharge—a distance between the electrodes of several centimeters, a radius of the enclosure of several centimeters and a pressure of several mm Hg.

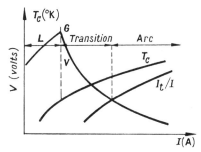

Fig. 13.1. Glow discharge—arc transition (in nitrogen, tungsten cathode). (J. D. COBINE, *Gaseous Conductors*, Dover, 1957, p. 312.) L — region of glow discharge; I_c—thermionic saturation current; I—total cathode current; T_c—cathode temperature

13.3.2 Spark

It is also possible to achieve an arc system without passing through intermediary stable states such as the Townsend discharge and the glow discharge.

This is the case, for example, in gases at atmospheric pressure with a large electrode gap particularly when the p.d. applied exceeds the Paschen breakdown voltage: a spark bursts out and rapidly degenerates (10^{-6} sec) into an arc if the capacity of the current generator permits. This process, as opposed to the previous one, is irreversible.

Examples: lightning, insulation breakdown.

13.3.3 Electrodes in contact

If two electrodes initially in contact and crossed by a very intense current are separated, an arc is established between them which allows the current to be maintained.

In this case the p.d. between the electrodes never exceeds the low value characteristic of the arc.

Examples: interrupters, circuit breakers, etc.

13.4 Characteristics of the arc

13.4.1 V-I characteristic

The *V-I* characteristic of an arc does not have a negative slope throughout. It always ends by inverting at high currents.

Moreover, the dynamic characteristic differs a great deal from the static characteristic. If the operation of the arc is sufficiently fast, neither the pressure nor the temperature have time to assume their steady state values which are often only set up after several minutes.

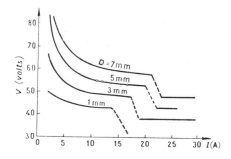

Fig. 13.2. Carbon arc in atmospheric air. Distance between electrodes—*D* (mm). (J. D. COBINE, *op. cit.*, p. 293)

13.4.2 Distribution of potential along the arc

Figures 13.3 and 13.4 show that there is a uniform positive column (*E* = constant) in long arcs just as there is in luminous discharges.

A cathode region and potential drop and an anode region and potential drop can also be observed but it is not easy to analyze them as they only extend over very small distances.

In general, the cathode fall in potential predominates. It is of the order of magnitude of the ionization potential of the gas in question and of the vapor of the element of which the cathode is made (see Table 13.1 compiled by I. LANGMUIR and H. MOTT-SMITH, *Gen. Elec. Rev.*, 27, 762, 1924).

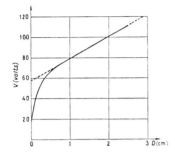

Fig. 13.3. Carbon arc in atmospheric air for $I = 7$ A. (A. von ENGEL, *op. cit.*, p. 23)

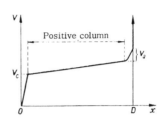

Fig. 13.4

Table 13.1. Properties of arcs at $p = 1$ atm

Electrodes	gas	I (A)	T_c (°K)	T_a (°K)	j_c (A/cm²)	j_a (A/cm²)	V_c (V)	V_a (V)
C - C	air	1 - 10	3,500	4,200	470	65	9 - 11	11 - 12
C - C	N_2	4 - 10	3,500	4,000	500	70		
Cu - Cu	air, N_2	~ 5	$<2,200$	2,400	$\sim 10^6$	$\sim 10^3$	8 - 9	2 - 6
Fe - Fe	air	~ 5	2,400	2,600	large		8 - 12	2 - 6
Ni - Ni	air	~ 5	2,400	2,400				
W - W	air	~ 5	3,000	4,200				
Al - Al	air	~ 5	3,400	3,400				
Al - Al	N_2	~ 5	$\sim 2,500$	$\sim 2,500$				
Zn - Zn	air	~ 5	3,000	3,000				
Zn - Zn	N_2	~ 5	small	small				

13.4.3 Form of arc

This varies depending on the pressure and the current. In general, the positive column is very luminous. Close to the electrodes it contracts and forms extremely luminous spots or patches. The electrodes reach an incandescent state and rapidly evaporate. The emission spectrum of the positive column contains lines characteristic of the material of the electrodes.

The gas between the electrodes is raised to a very high temperature when the pressure is fairly high; it then becomes the seat of convection currents. The cross section of the column can vary from one point to another and with time.

Example: Fig. 13.5.

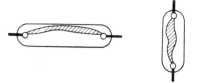

Fig. 13.5. Convection effects

13.5 The positive column

As in the glow discharge, the positive column of the arc is made up of a plasma; the electric field in it is small and relatively homogeneous. From this it is deduced that the positive and negative charges neutralize on a macroscopic scale: $n_e \approx n_i \approx n$. They have velocities due to thermal agitation which are large in comparison with their drift velocity (due to diffusion of concentration or displacement due to the field).

The properties of the column of an arc differ little from those of the glow column as long as the current density is not very high and the pressure does not exceed 0.1 atm (low-pressure arc).

We shall now investigate the development of the positive column as a function of the two principal parameters, pressure and current.

13.5.1 Temperatures T_e, T_i, T_g

As the positive ions and neutral molecules of the gas have more or less the same mass, they exchange energy readily. As there are a large number of molecules, molecule-molecule and ion-molecule collisions occur frequently. A state of equilibrium is rapidly established, the temperatures T_g and T_i of the gas and ions merging. In fact, T_i is slightly higher than T_g because, between two collisions, the ions are accelerated by the electric field.

Negative ions are rare and play no part of any importance.

Thanks to the mobility of the electrons, it is they which absorb most energy from the electric field. They impart some of this to the ions and molecules by elastic and inelastic collisions. The former heat the gas while the latter excite and ionize it. The collisional frequency depends chiefly on the temperature of the electrons (since the electrons are always faster than the other particles): cf. Fig. 13.6 and Chapters 3 and 4.

Figure 13.7 is derived from Fig. 13.6 and the mean energy transferred in each collision. At low pressures, the density of neutral particles diminishes. To maintain a given discharge current,

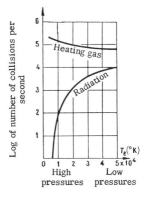

Fig. 13.6. Frequency of elastic and inelastic collisions in mercury vapor at a fixed pressure; assuming $n_e = n_i$. The units of the ordinate are arbitrary. (T. WASSERAB, Z. Phys., **127**, 324, 1950)

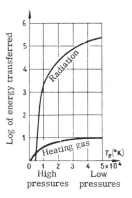

Fig. 13.7. Energy given to the mercury atoms by the electrons in inelastic and elastic collisions. Arbitrary units for ordinate. (T. WASSERAB, Z. Phys., **127**, 324, 1950)

the number of ionizing collisions must be increased. T_e must therefore increase (see Fig. 13.8). But then the fraction of energy lost by the electrons in elastic collisions decreases considerably and thus T_g decreases. Conversely, when the pressure increases, T_e decreases and $T_g \approx T_i$ increases until $T_e \approx T_i \approx T_g$. This can be seen in Fig. 13.8. The temperature of an arc may reach some tens of thousands of degrees at low pressures.

The temperature distribution as a function of the distance from the axis is given in Fig. 13.9 for various pressures.

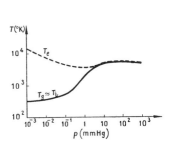

Fig. 13.8. The three temperatures in the positive column

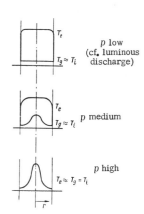

Fig. 13.9. Radial distribution of temperatures in the positive column

It can be seen that at medium and high pressures T depends strongly on the distance from the axis. In effect, the energy losses due to thermal conductivity to the walls (cold) are no longer negligible.

When the discharge current I increases, the number of free charges n rises and, as a result, the frequency of their collisions also rises. This as a whole produces the same effects as raising the pressure.

13.5.2 Density of electric charge

At low pressures, the theory of the luminous discharge is valid. At high pressures, when all the temperatures are the same, there is equilibrium in a thermodynamical sense (complete equilibrium) and the degree of ionization is determined by the law of mass action expressed by Saha in the form

$$\frac{x^2}{1 - x^2} p = 2{,}4 \cdot 10^{-4} \ T^{5/2} \exp(- eV_i/kT)$$

where

$x = n_e/N = n_i/N$
$T = T_e = T_i = T_g$
p = pressure (in mm Hg)
V_i = ionization potential of the gas
N = density of particles (neutrons, ions, electrons)

This relation is illustrated in Fig. 13.10.

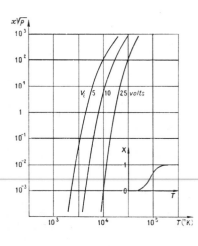

Fig. 13.10. Degree of ionization x as a function of the temperature T at high pressures (p in mm Hg, V_i = ionization potential of the gas). (A. von ENGEL, *Ionized Gases*, Clarendon Press, 1955, p. 70)

It can be seen that the degree of ionization and, in general, the charge density should diminish rapidly towards the boundaries of the column.

Orders of magnitude: $n = 10^{10}$ cm^{-3} (low pressures) to 10^{18} (very high pressures); 10^{14} to 10^{16} at atmospheric pressure and at I = several amperes.

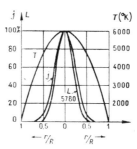

Fig. 13.11. Radial distribution of temperature T, current density j (proportional to the charge density n) and the intensity of the 5780-Å line in a Hg vapor arc at 1 atm. (W. ELENBAAS, *The High Pressure Mercury Vapor Discharge*, North Holland, 1951)

13.5.3 Axial electric field

It is from this that the electrons gain the energy necessary to ionize and excite the gas, and it is this which compensates the losses due to radiation, conduction, etc.

The electric field E will therefore be much greater in molecular gases than in atomic gases since the former absorb more energy by dissociation and the excitation of vibrations and rotations (cf. Section 12.2.5.3).

In general, E increases with pressure since the probability of collisions increases with the particle density (Fig. 13.12).

At pressures close to 1 atm, E may thus reach several tens of V/cm. It should be noted that E diminishes as I increases (the charge density compensates for the diminution in their acceleration).

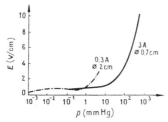

Fig. 13.12. Variations in the longitudinal electric field in the positive column for two arc tubes with different diameters. (J. M. SOMMERVILLE, *The Electric Arc*, Methuen, 1959, p. 23)

13.5.4 Energy balance

The energy supplied by the electric field is carried off:

1. through the walls by (a) emission of atomic and molecular band and line spectra, and (b) bremsstrahlung;

2. by heating the walls and conduction of heat through them to the ambient gas and the supports. The walls are heated by the effects of:

(a) the impact of ions and electrons accelerated by the field,

(b) the recombination of ions and electrons on the walls (exothermic phenomenon),

(c) the deexcitation of metastable atoms on contact with the walls,

(d) recombination of dissociated molecules at the walls, and

(e) the impact of neutral molecules (thermal conduction).

Figure 13.13 represents the variations of the proportions of these different processes as a function of the pressure.

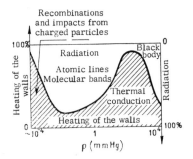

Fig. 13.13. Energy balance for a mercury arc

14 dielectric strength of gases
steady field

All substances have some resistance to the passage of electricity whether this resistance be large or small and whether it be highly or only slightly variable. Those which have a high resistance are called insulators or dielectrics. But these bodies do not have an infinite dielectric strength. When the electric field acting on them reaches a sufficiently high value, they abruptly allow the passage of a very intense current in the form of a spark or an arc: they become highly conducting. The p.d. of the two electrodes at which this electric field is set up is said to be the breakdown voltage, this p.d. being measured immediately prior to the breakdown of the dielectric. For a given dielectric, the breakdown voltage depends on the experimental conditions: temperature, pressure, nature and form of the electrodes, law of variation of the voltage with time, ambient radiation.

All these considerations also naturally apply to gases.

In Chapter 11, we studied the breakdown of a gas at medium pressures between two plane, parallel, infinite (uniform electric field) electrodes to which was applied a slowly varying voltage. Under these conditions, the breakdown strength of the dielectric is governed by the Townsend criterion and the Paschen law.

We shall now see how this law is modified under the normal conditions found in practice which usually differ from the ideal conditions considered previously. These modifications consist of:

(a) a change in the mechanism of breakdown;
(b) a voltage function $V = f$ (p or d) instead of $f(pd)$.

14.1 Review of the breakdown conditions

The necessary and, in general, sufficient conditions for break-down are:

1. the existence of an initial free electric charge between the electrodes;

2. the existence of a discontinuity in the multiplication factor for the ·electric charges. This discontinuity occurs when the charges liberated by the passage of the initial charge are capable, on average, of giving rise to a particle identical to the initial particle under the same initial conditions before disappearing at the walls or electrodes. Even if the cause of ionization disappears, the current then continues to pass—the discharge is self-sustaining. Mathematically this means that the coefficient of multiplication is infinite.

If the external source of ionization continues to act, the current rapidly increases to a value limited only by the external circuit.

The first condition is always satisfied sooner or later by the passage of a ionizing particle of cosmic origin. The same result can be obtained artificially by means of X-rays, atomic radiation, flames, etc.

The second condition is fulfilled in different ways depending on the particular case (nature of the applied voltage, gas pressure, form of the electrodes, etc.). We shall first consider the case of a constant or continuously increasing voltage [the case of HF (high frequency) discharges will be dealt with later].

The initial electron crosses the space between the electrodes in a time which depends on the gas, its density, the distance between the electrodes and the electric field; this time may be very short (example: 5×10^{-9} sec for $d = 1$ mm). In the course of its trajectory, it gives rise to an avalanche of secondary electrons which accompany it and of positive ions and photons; this multiplication effect is governed by the first Townsend coefficient: α.

Since α is constant, breakdown can only occur if, before disappearing, this first avalanche itself gives rise to a second avalanche at least as dense, and so on. This can only happen thanks to other processes for the production of free charges. Several of these are known and others can be imagined:

1. β effect: ionization of the gas by positive ions created by the initial electron. Townsend originally invoked this process to explain the breakdown but later recognized that this did not agree with the facts.

2. γ effect: emission of secondary electrons by the cathode under impact from ions in the discharge. It is this process which explains breakdown at medium pressures (see Chapter 11). It depends on the nature of the gas and the cathode and can only occur after a considerable delay.

3. δ effect: emission of secondary electrons by the cathode under impact from photons coming from the discharge (de-excitation or recombination). Since the photons are very fast and scarcely absorbed, this process is very rapid and efficient (particularly at high pressures); it depends on the gas and the cathode.

4. ε effect: emission of secondary electrons by the cathode under impact from excited atoms in a metastable state. The effect is analogous to γ and δ processes but in this case the delay is a great deal longer because the atoms diffuse very slowly to the cathode.

5. η effect: photo-ionization of the gas. The process can only play a significant part at very high pressures. It can only occur in pure gases (particularly monoatomic) with difficulty as the photons which arise in the gas due to recombination or deexcitation do not have an energy sufficient to ionize the same gas.

6. σ effect: effect of space charge. When the applied pressure or voltage is very high, the density of charges of each sign rapidly assumes a value such that the field is strongly perturbed. Beyond a certain threshold, it would be possible for the ionization of the space between the electrons to rise sharply thus permitting a spark to occur. Raëther and Meek invoke this process in their theories relating to canals and streamers (see below).

These processes, and perhaps others, occur separately or simultaneously depending on the circumstances. It is they which determine the development of the voltage and current of the discharge from the moment at which the first free charge is created in the electric field.

14.2 Region of applicability of Townsend's criterion and of Paschen's law

In Chapter 11 we obtained the condition for a Townsend breakdown taking into account only the γ secondary effect.

This result can be generalized to take into account the δ and ε effects. The condition for breakdown then becomes

$$\boxed{C(e^{\alpha d} - 1) = 1}$$
(14.1)

with $C = \gamma + (\delta + \varepsilon)/\alpha$ = second Townsend coefficient.

If the β and η effects are not very intense, they can also be included in the above expression so that

$$C = \gamma + \frac{\beta + \delta + \varepsilon + \eta}{\alpha}$$
(14.2)

Experiment shows that, making this generalization, Townsend's criterion remains valid from $pd \approx 10^{-2}\text{-}10^{-1}$ cm mm Hg to $pd \approx 1000$ cm mm Hg.

But Townsend's condition was obtained by calculating the multiplication factor for an electron leaving the cathode in a constant electric field and in a steady state; mathematically, this signifies that all the terms of the series

$$e^{\alpha d}[1 + C(e^{\alpha d} - 1) + C^2(e^{\alpha d} - 1)^2 + \cdots]$$

are taken.

Physically, this means there must be a large number of avalanches. Since each avalanche has a finite duration, the steady state is only established after a time which is by no means negligible. When the condition for breakdown is reached, this series is no longer convergent; each avalanche is more dense than the previous one. After several avalanches, breakdown is said to have occurred.

It is obvious that this does not depend only on the voltage applied, but also on the point and instant at which the initial electric charge appears as well as on the electric field and its variations with time.

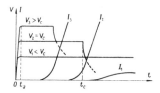

Fig. 14.1. t_a = appearance of initial electron; t_c = breakdown; $t_c - t_a = t_f$ = formation time. (F. LLEWELLYN JONES, *Ionization and Breakdown in Gases*, Methuen, 1957)

To study the breakdown voltage, in practice, the cathode is subjected to high-energy radiation (X-rays or U.V.). It can then be assumed that the initial electron appears at the cathode. At time 0 (Fig. 14.1), a voltage V is briefly applied (time of application $< 10^{-8}$ or 10^{-9} sec). If the breakdown does not occur after a short interval, the experiment is repeated with a slightly increased value of V. Breakdown eventually appears when $V = V_c$ in the form of a sharp rise in the current accompanied by an abrupt and very large drop in the p.d. between the electrodes at time t_c. It is assumed that the delay t_a between the time when the voltage is applied $(t = o)$ and the electron appears on the cathode $(t = t_a = $ waiting time) is very short. The time for the formation of the discharge is defined as

$$t_f = t_c - t_a$$

and therefore differs little from t_c. This is the only factor which depends on the mechanism of the discharge and can provide information as to its nature. The waiting time, on the other hand, only depends on the conditions of irradiation of the cathode (if the electric field at the surface is not high enough to extract electrons).

The smallest breakdown voltage measured under the above conditions is termed the static breakdown voltage. At higher voltages, t_f diminishes as V increases (Fig. 14.2).

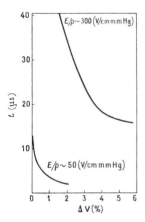

Fig. 14.2. Formation time as a function of the excess voltage $\Delta V = (V - V_c)/V_c \times 100$ (hydrogen at low pressure). (F. LLEWELLYN JONES, *Ionization and Breakdown in Gases*, Methuen, p. 139, 1957)

By comparing the measured values of t_f at different V with the calculated values and making different hypotheses as to the mechanism of breakdown, it is possible to draw certain conclusions as to which mechanism is the most probable. These investigations are complementary to a comparison between the measured values of V_c and those calculated using the Townsend criterion or any other criterion such as that of Meek or Raëther.

Thus Llewellyn Jones and his colleagues have shown that, in the interval $10^{-2} < pd < 10^3$ mm Hg cm, the generalized Townsend mechanism is sufficient to explain values of t_f of the order of 10^{-6} sec for excess voltages of several percent.

But experiment shows that, at very high excess voltages, t_f may be reduced to extremely low values possibly even smaller than the transit time for an avalanche ($0.6 \cdot 10^{-9}$ sec for $d = 1$ mm).

To explain this phenomenon, the Townsend effect is no longer sufficient. Other processes must come into play.

The interest of investigations into the development of a discharge under a high excess voltage lies in the fact that new mechanisms can be seen at work.

It was this that led Raëther, Loeb and Meek to propose their canal and streamer mechanisms.

Their theories are based on the following observations:

1. Certain experimental results show that the breakdown voltage in air at a pressure of several atmospheres does not vary very much with the nature of the cathode.

2. At high excess voltages, the discharge current reaches high values before the first avalanche has disappeared (and a fortiori before the ions from this avalanche have reached the cathode and extracted secondary electrons from it).

3. The discharge is no longer diffuse, as in the case of the Townsend discharge, but is concentrated in a narrow canal with branches and abrupt changes in direction (spark).

4. In the path of this canal, the charge density should notably perturb the initial electric field. In fact, in the case of air at NTP with $d = 1$ cm, $V_c = 32$ kV, $E/p = 45$ V/cm mm Hg, $\eta = 6.10^{-4}$ and exp $(\eta V_c) \approx 10^3$. But if $V/V_c = 1.3$, exp $(\eta V) \approx 10^{21}$! $(N \approx 2.10^{19}$ cm$^{-3} < 10^{21}$ cm$^{-3})$.

Under these conditions, the process illustrated in Fig. 14.3 can be imagined.

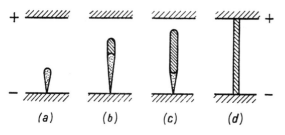

Fig. 14.3. Formation of a canal or streamer. (a) Beginnings of an avalanche due to an electron; (b) formation of a conducting plasma at the head of the avalanche directed towards the anode; (c) the plasma "canal" begins to move back towards the cathode as well as advancing to the anode; (d) "canal" established between the anode and cathode

In (b), the space charge due to the positive ions (which are practically immobile) has become strong enough to subtract from the avalanche a number of electrons sufficient to neutralize it locally: a trail of plasma is formed behind the avalanche. According to Meek, the trail begins to form when the space charge field $\approx$ the initial field. Raëther showed that the number of charges in the avalanche must reach $N_c = 10^8$ to 10^{10}. The trail appears earlier and the point at which it appears is closer to the cathode as the voltage increases and the pressure rises.

The rear portion of this trail perturbs the electric field and strongly attracts to itself all electrons liberated by photo-ionization of the gas (η effect). New avalanches are thus formed which rapidly extend the plasma canal towards the cathode in a more or less undulating line. An analogous process takes place on the anode side.

In (d) the canal of conducting plasma is completed and the discharge established.

The various stages of this process have been photographed by Raëther in a Wilson cloud chamber.

Notes:

1. This process does not occur in pure, rare or atomic gases (probably due to the absence of any η effect).
2. It is only possible if the distance between the electrodes is sufficient for the charge density of the avalanche to reach a critical value n_c.
3. $N_c = \exp[(\alpha d)_c]$. Thus Raëther's criterion has much the same form as Townsend's: $C \exp[(\alpha d)_c] = 1$. In this case, $(\alpha d)_c \approx 20$.

14.3 Effect of pressure

14.3.1 Very high pressures (pd > 1000 cm mm Hg)

Paschen's law states that, for a given distance between the electrodes, the breakdown voltage is higher the greater the pressure. Insulation techniques are largely based on this fact (insulation of Van de Graaf generators and hard X-ray generators).

But experiment shows that for $pd \gg 1000$ cm mm Hg, Paschen's law is modified in an "unfavorable" manner. Figure 14.4 shows that, at constant pd, V_c decreases as p increases, and decreases more rapidly the higher pd.

Figure 14.5 also shows that:

1. the breakdown voltage is only fixed to within a few percent;
2. it depends to a large extent on the nature of the electrodes.

Since the γ and δ cathode effects seem to be very weak at these pressures, it must be concluded that some other process strongly affected by the cathode is involved. Since Paschen's law is no longer fulfilled, it cannot be any of the usual processes: β, ε, η, which all depend on E/p.

At the same time, it does not seem possible to assume there is a space charge effect since this would be independent of the nature of the cathode; moreover, calculations based on this hypothesis only lead to insignificant deviations from Paschen's law.

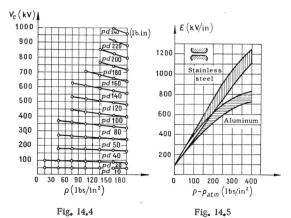

Fig. 14.4   Fig. 14.5

Breakdown in air at very high pressure (10 lb x in ≈ 1,300 cm
mm Hg; 1 lb/in² ≈ 50 mm Hg). (F. LLEWELLYN JONES, *op. cit.*,
pp. 99 and 100)

Certain authors have shown that, in the region in question, the
electric field is very intense; for example, p = 100 atm, d = 0.1 mm,
pd = 760 mm Hg cm, E = 3.10⁶ V/cm. It would therefore be
possible for field emission to contribute to the discharge. We
shall discuss the likelihood of this explanation further on.

14.3.2 Very low pressures (pd < 10⁻² cm mm Hg)

The Paschen curves show that, when pd is lower than the value
corresponding to the minimum value for the breakdown voltage
V_c, the latter increases as pd decreases. Physically speaking,
this is because the ratio d/λ tends to 1 and thus the probability of
ionizing collisions (coefficient α) diminishes in consequence.

But the breakdown mechanism involving a Townsend avalanche
occurs when $d/\lambda \gg 1$ (many ionizing collisions on the path of an
electron moving to the anode).

Now, at $pd \approx 10^{-2}$ cm mm Hg, $d/\lambda \approx 1$; the statistical coefficient
α no longer has much meaning and at values of $pd < 10^{-2}$ cm mm
Hg, deviations from Paschen's law are to be expected [$V_c = f(pd)$].

It can in fact be established that V_c no longer increases as p
decreases for constant d.

A new process of rapid increase in the discharge current must
be found to explain the breakdown. This process is probably
closely connected with the cathode; in fact, the secondary β and η
coefficients (which only depend on the gas) are very small in this
region and are practically negligible in comparison with γ and δ

(which depend to a large extent on the cathode). This is why the incluence of the cathode on the breakdown curves is felt more and more as p decreases (see Chapter 11).

Effect of electrodes

The electrodes have a large effect on breakdown at low pressures due to:

(a) their shape. In general, for a given small value of pd, d is so large for small p ($\sim 10^{-4}$ mm Hg, for example) that the electric field cannot be homogeneous ($d >$ dimensions of the electrodes). The field is particularly large at any roughness and may cause considerable cold emission;

(b) the state of their surfaces. V_c is larger the more highly polished the surface, probably for the same reasons as above. A rough, oxidized surface therefore favors breakdown;

(c) their nature. V_c is smaller the lower the work function (cf. Fig. 14.5).

These experimental results seem to indicate that field emission is the cause of certain breakdowns at low pressures as it is in the case of high pressure (Section 14.3.1).

However, all the measurements carried out lead to electric fields in the range 10^5 to several 10^6 V/cm at the moment of breakdown (see Figs. 14.6 and 14.7).

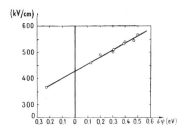

Fig. 14.6. Breakdown at very low pressure. Mercury cathode and molybdenum anode (∅ 20 mm). (L. R. QUARLES, *Phys. Rev.*, **48**, 260, 1936)

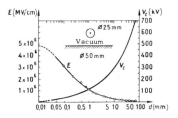

Fig. 14.7. Breakdown in a vacuum (J. G. TRUMP and R. J. VAN DE GRAAF, *J. Appl. Phys.*, **18**, 327, 1947)

As in the case of high pressures, the question is therefore whether such a field is sufficient to cause breakdown.

To find the answer to this question, the following experiment was carried out at atmospheric pressure: a voltage pulse $V \gtrsim 1.25$ V_c is applied to the electrodes for a time $\tau \sim 10^{-2}$ sec (Fig. 14.8). If no electron is emitted by the cathode during this time, nothing happens. It is assumed that if breakdown occurs (accompanied by a sharp drop in V) at time t_c, this corresponds to the extraction

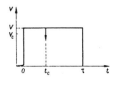

Fig 14.8

of an electron. If it is assumed that the probability of the extraction of an electron during time dt is $I\,dt$, then the probability that no electron will be extracted before time t_c is $\exp(-\,I\,t_c)$ and

$$I = 1/(\bar{t_c})$$

electrons per unit time, or

$$I = \frac{1}{t}\log(N/n)$$

N = total number of tests; n = number of tests for which $t_c \geqslant t$.
A summary of the results is given in the following table:

Table 14.1. Electrons emitted per second for $V \approx 10^4$ V/cm
(atmospheric pressure)

Steel			Copper		Nickel	Al-Mg alloy
Milled	Oxidized	Turned	Drawn	Turned	Turned	Turned
10^6	10^6	5.5×10^3	1.4×10^4	5×10^5	7×10^3	5×10^3

It can be seen that the emission is far from being negligible. These results also confirm, in general, the influence of the electrodes as pointed out above.

It also demonstrates a conditioning effect: when the breakdown current is limited to fairly low values, the emission I decreases as the number of tests increase. This would be due to the successive elimination of dust and microscopic irregularities.

In conclusion, it would appear that I varies with E according to the law for cold emission:

$$I = A E^2 \exp(-\,B/E)$$

but with coefficients A and B such that the work function $\varphi \approx 1$ eV and the effective surface area $S \approx 10^{-14}$ cm^2. These results suggest the mechanism of very localized field emission.

Certain authors have suggested effects other than field emission:

(a) local vaporization of the cathode under ion bombardment;
(b) distortion of the potential barrier by the ions trapped in the surface insulating layer (cf. Malter effect);
(c) secondary emission of ions and photons from the anode under bombardment by electrons and secondary emission of electrons by the cathode under bombardment by these ions and photons.

14.4 Effect of distance

Various kinds of relays and interrupters are the seat of sparks which may be very short. Study of these has led experimenters to analyze the conditions for a discharge between electrodes separated by 10^{-7} to 10^{-4} cm.

The most remarkable feature of this region is the small value of V_c: between 1 and 100 V, that is to say, well below the Paschen minimum.

In this case the effect of the cathode is again very important. Breakdown appears to be impossible in the absence of a surface layer of oxide or dust.

Certain authors are of the opinion that field emission again plays the leading part.

14.5 Effect of magnetic fields

14.5.1 Longitudinal magnetic field (parallel to E)

The principal effect of such a field is to reduce the loss of electrons by diffusion out of the space between the electrodes (see Chapter 8, $D_\perp = D_0/[1 + (\omega_c \tau)^2]$). When the pressure is too small and the m.f.p. greater than or equal to the distance between the electrons, the concept of diffusion is no longer applicable; however, the fact remains that electrons leaving the cathode at oblique angles are obliged to describe spirals with axes parallel to the magnetic field and with a radius proportional to $1/B$, which again prevents them from moving outwards.

Thus the breakdown voltage can be diminished by applying a longitudinal magnetic field.

The Penning ionization gauge (P.I.G. or Philips ionization gauge) is based on this principle (see Fig. 14.9).

The disposition of the electrodes forces the electrons to cross from one cathode to the other several times and the magnetic field prevents them from diffusing laterally.

During the course of its existence, a single electron thus produces a large number of ionizing collisions. The discharge current is a measure of the pressure between the electrodes. It remains quite high right down to pressures of 10^{-5} mm Hg.

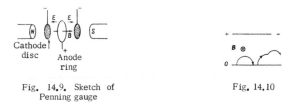

Fig. 14.9. Sketch of
Penning gauge

Fig. 14.10

14.5.2 *Transverse magnetic field*
(perpendicular to E)

In this case the electrons have difficulty in approaching the anode (Fig. 14.10). The effect is the same as a very high pressure. Depending on whether this occurs to the left or the right of the Paschen minimum (for **B** = 0), the breakdown voltage will therefore be reduced or increased by application of the magnetic field.

14.6 Effect of temperature

Although Paschen's law gives rise to the product pd, this is only due to the fact that most experiments are carried out at a constant temperature (ambient temperature). In fact what is important is the total number of molecules in collision with an electron on its path from the cathode to the anode. This number is proportional to nd or ρd where n and ρ are respectively the particle and mass densities of the gas at the prevailing temperature and pressure.

14.7 Effect of the geometry of the electrodes
(breakdown in nonuniform fields)

In practice, the electric field between two electrodes is never uniform and the above considerations cannot be rigorously applied. We shall only consider the simplest geometries used: cylindrical; circular; plane parallel; coaxial; spherical and pointed electrodes (in the latter case the point being effectively terminated by a hemisphere of very small radius).

A very large number of results have been obtained for these geometries and these are of great use. However, it is difficult to interpret these results for two reasons:

1. Since E/p is no longer constant, α/p which depends on it varies in a manner which is often very complex. The relations $\alpha/p = f(E/p)$ obtained for uniform fields are only true in the steady state, that is to say, once the electrons have reached their limit of drift velocity. These relations therefore cannot be applied to a field that varies too rapidly with distance.

2. In the cases of extreme inhomogeneity, the ionization is so strong where the field is intense that the resultant space charge perturbs the field to a large extent, thus making it impossible to make a mathematical analysis.

This is why we shall concentrate on experimental results in the following.

These results are remarkable from several points of view:

1. They differ greatly depending on the polarity of the applied voltage: there is asymmetry of polarity.

2. They depend to a large extent on the electrode with the smallest radius of curvature because it is in the neighborhood of this that the field is highest.

3. They depend very little on the distance between the electrodes, which only appears in the form of a logarithmic function.

14.7.1 Coaxial and bifilar arrangements

Description of phenomena. Let a thin, smooth wire F of radius a be mounted along the axis of a cylinder C of radius b, both having a long length (see Fig. 14.11). The cylinder is filled with gas at a pressure p. When the p.d. reaches a value V_c (breakdown voltage), a luminous sheath appears about the wire; at the same time, a characteristic crackling is heard and ozone is formed in the air. This is the corona effect.

Fig. 14.11

Fig. 14.12. Positive and negative corona

If the wire is raised to a positive potential with respect to the cylinder C, it is surrounded by a large hazy sheath (positive corona, Fig. 14.12); in air, this sheath is bluish white.

If, on the other hand, the wire F is negative with respect to C, regularly spaced, brilliant, short, reddish sprays are observed along its length. At fairly low pressures, the sprays merge into a more or less continuous sheath.

If the p.d. is alternating, the above phenomena can be observed alternately every half period. The same thing happens with two parallel wires (bifilar geometry).

"Breakdown" field. The potential difference between F and C is given as a function of the electric field E_F at the surface of F by the well-known relation:

$$V = E_F \, a \log (b/a)$$

The condition for breakdown is defined by E_F rather than V since E_F is independent of other parameters. In the case of alternating p.d.'s ($10 < f < 10{,}000$ c/s), Peel has obtained empirically the following condition:

$$(\hat{E}_F)_c = 31 \, m\delta \left(1 + \frac{0.308}{\sqrt{\delta a}}\right) \text{kV/cm} \tag{14.3}$$

where

$\hat{E}$ = peak value of alternating field

m = empirical coefficient depending on the surface of the wire lying in the range 0.6 to 1 (see Table 14.2)

$\delta = \dfrac{3.92 \, p}{273 + t}$

p = gas pressure in cm Hg

t = temperature in °C

This relation is valid from pressures of a few cm Hg up to several atmospheres.

Note: $\delta = 1$ for air at N.T.P.

Table 14.2. Coefficient m

State of surface	m
Rough.	0.67 - 0.74
Dusty	0.72 - 0.75
Scoured.	0.91 - 0.93
Polished. . . .	1

With bifilar geometry (two parallel wires of radius a separated by $d \gg a$),

$$V = 2 \, E_F \, a \ln (d/a)$$

and

$$(\hat{E}_F)_c = 30 \, m\delta \left(1 + \frac{0.301}{\sqrt{\delta a}}\right) \text{kV/cm} \qquad (14.4)$$

with the same notation as above.

Note:

1. Relations 14.3 and 14.4 are almost identical. This is connected with the fact that (E_F) depends only on the thin electrode provided the other is sufficiently removed from it.

2. For air at atmospheric pressure and at normal temperature,

$$(\hat{E}_F)_c \approx 30 \, (1 + 0.3/\sqrt{a}) \text{ kV/cm}$$

while, for a uniform field, $E_c \approx 30$ kV/cm $\leqslant (E_F)_c$.

3. The values of $(E_F)_c$ given by Peel probably correspond to the appearance of the negative corona.

If the applied p.d. is steady, there is a sharp difference between the breakdown voltages for the positive and negative coronas. In general, $(E_F)_c$ is smaller when the thin electrode is negative (see Figs. 14.13 and 14.14).

This polarity effect can be used to rectify alternating current.

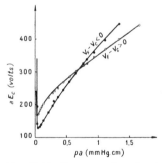

Fig. 14.13. Characteristics of positive and negative coronas in air. (F. LLEWELLYN JONES, *op. cit.*, p. 117)

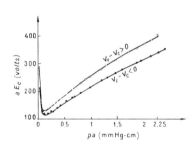

Fig. 14.14. Characteristics of positive and negative coronas in hydrogen. (F. LLEWELLYN JONES, *op. cit.*, p. 118)

Note: From all this it follows that V_c depends only on ap (since $V_c \approx a \, E_F.f \, (\ln a) \approx \text{Const.} \, a.E_F$).

To avoid the corona effect at medium and high pressures all that is therefore necessary in general is to increase the radius of curvature of the thin or pointed conductors. This has applications such as to electric power transmission lines.

Analysis of the corona effect. Up to now it has been assumed that the criterion for the appearance of the corona effect is of the same form as Townsend's criterion (see Section 14.2).

$$1 - C\left[\exp\left(\int_a^b \alpha(r)\,dr\right) - 1\right] = 0$$

or

$$1 \approx C \exp\left(\int_a^b \alpha(r)\,dr\right)$$

Since α increases greatly with E and $E \approx$ Const./r, ionization will only be significant in the immediate vicinity of the wire, that is to say, $a < r < c$ (Fig. 14.15), where c is roughly defined by $E(c) =$ breakdown field for plane parallel infinite electrodes. It is this region which determines the breakdown conditions.

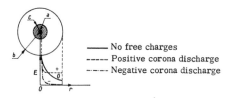

——— No free charges
----- Positive corona discharge
–·–·– Negative corona discharge

Fig. 14.15. Electric field with and without discharge

When the wire is negative, this region is the seat of electron avalanches, as in a homogeneous field. C is then simply equal to γ since the γ effect is reinforced while the others are diminished (small cathode surface area). The region adjacent to the wire contains a strong positive space charge which practically cancels out the field at $r > c$. Beyond c the electrons can thus no longer ionize the gas; they attach themselves to neutral particles and continue on their path to the anode. It is they alone that transfer the electric current once the discharge is established.

When the wire is positive, it attracts the electrons but they cannot ionize the gas until they have acquired sufficient energy, that is to say until they are in the region of the wire. In this case, the secondary processes which maintain the discharge are probably β, δ and η effects. The positive ions which are attracted by the cylindrical cathode arrive at it with a drift velocity too small to cause any significant secondary emission. In this case, once the discharge has been established, the current between c and b is principally made up of a single space charge provided there are positive ions.

On the basis of the above considerations it is possible to calculate the characteristics $I = f(V)$ for a corona discharge. It is quadratic as follows:

$$I = \frac{2\,\mu}{b^2 \ln(b/a)}\ (V - V_c)\,V$$

where μ = mobility of the ions (+ or −) which constitute the current between c and b; $V = V_F - V_C$ CGS ESU.

Since $\mu_+ \approx \mu_-$, the "positive and negative" characteristics are very similar.

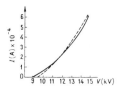

Fig. 14.16. Characteristics for positive (——) or negative (- - -) discharge. a = 0.2 mm; b = 22.3 mm; T = 25°C; relative humidity = 29.2%; p = 747 mm Hg. (J. D. COBINE, *Gaseous Conductors*, Dover, 1958, p. 259)

The corona effect is, of course, accompanied by a loss in energy from the source of p.d. This loss corresponds to radiation from the discharge, to elastic and inelastic collisions in the surrounding gas and at the surface of the electrodes. In electric transmission lines, these losses may be equal to the losses due to the Joule effect in the conductors.

14.7.2 Pointed electrodes

The behavior is very similar to that of wire electrodes and the general conclusions are the same in both cases.

REFERENCES FOR CHAPTERS 14 AND 15

LLEWELLYN JONES, *Ionization and Breakdown in Gases* (Methuen Monograph, 1957).
MEEK and CRAGGS, *Electrical Breakdown of Gases* (Oxford, 1953).
S. C. BROWN, *Basic Data of Plasma Physics* (J. Wiley, 1960).
J. D. COBINE, *Gaseous Conductors* (Dover, 1958).

M

15 dielectric strength of gases—
high-frequency breakdown

Like all physical phenomena, gaseous discharges may be associated with a time constant, τ, which defines the duration of the transitory state preceding the establishment of the steady state. If the p.d., V, applied to the gaseous dielectric varies with time, the same phenomena as for continuous current will be observed provided that the variation in V in the time τ is small. Naturally this does not exclude hysteresis: the sequence of phenomena during the decrease in V is not the exact inverse of those observed during the increase in V. Thus the p.d. at the extinction of the discharge is slightly less than the p.d. at the start. As to the fundamental processes involved, these remain the same as in the case of continuous current discharges.

However, when the p.d. alternates with a fairly high frequency (with respect to $1/\tau$), the mechanism of discharge may be modified. In fact, at HF (high frequency) three or four types of discharge can be distinguished, and it is these which are the subject of the present chapter.

15.1 Experimental apparatus

Figure 15.1 represents the three main types of apparatus which can be used to produce HF discharges.

The discharge tube (15.1a) is analogous to the classical tube used for continuous current. In this case the voltage is still applied to two electrodes but these may be mounted either inside or outside the gas enclosure. The electrodes may be plane and parallel or cylindrical and coaxial or cylindrical and parallel.

In (15.1b) there are no electrodes in the usual sense. The discharge is induced by an intense current passing through a solenoid surrounding the enclosure. Note that the latter may be metallic provided that its thickness is less than the ''skin depth'' under the experimental conditions; the electromagnetic field can then penetrate into the gas.

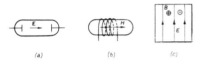

Fig. 15.1. HF discharge tubes: (a) with two plane electrodes; (b) induction; (c) metal cavity

In a metal cavity excited by an antenna (15.1c), the distribution of the electric and magnetic fields essentially depends on the form of the cavity and also on the type of antenna. The intensity of the fields is only large in the vicinity of the resonance frequency. The corresponding wavelength is of the order of magnitude of the geometrical dimensions of the cavity. Reasonable dimensions (of the order of a few decimeters at the most) correspond to very high frequencies (of the order of 1000 Mc/s at least).

In the case of alternating current, the electric and magnetic fields cannot be dissociated from one another. However, the longer the wavelength, the more they become localized at different points in space. Thus at frequencies of less than one megacycle per second, the magnetic field can be neglected in an apparatus of type (a) (E-type discharges) and the electric field in the apparatus of type (b) (H-type discharges). The latter are used up to about 100 MC/s. However, apparatus of type (a) is, of course, preferable to any other since its simpler geometry facilitates the interpretation of the results.

The conditions for the establishment and maintenance of an HF discharge depend not only on the distribution of the fields and their frequency but also on the pressure and nature of the gas inside the receptacle, the dimensions of the latter, the nature of its walls and also any continuous field (electric or magnetic) superimposed on the HF field.

In general, the pressure does not exceed a few cm Hg and, for the sake of simplicity, we shall limit ourselves to the case where the continuous field is zero.

In addition, we shall ignore the steady state of the discharge in order to concentrate on the breakdown mechanisms.

15.2 Motion of an electron under the influence of a uniform a.c. field

15.2.1 In vacuum or a very rarefied gas

Let $E = E_0 \sin (\omega t + \theta)$ be the electric field, m the mass, e the charge, v_0 the initial velocity and x the displacement of an electron parallel to E ($x = x_0$ at $t = 0$); then

$$m\, \ddot{x} = e\, E_0 \sin (\omega t + \theta)$$

and integrating

$$\dot{x} = v_0 + \frac{e\, E_0}{m\omega} \left[\cos \theta - \cos (\omega t + \theta)\right] \tag{15.1}$$

then

$$\boxed{\begin{aligned} x = x_0 + \left(v_0 + \frac{e\, E_0}{m\,\omega} \cos \theta\right) t \\ + \frac{e\, E_0}{m\omega^2} \left[\sin \theta - \sin (\omega t + \theta)\right] \end{aligned}} \tag{15.2}$$

Any transverse component of the initial velocity remains unaffected by E. Figure 15.2 illustrates the situation.

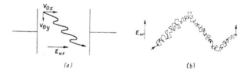

Fig. 15.2. Motion of an electron in an HF field: (a) at very low pressures ($\nu \ll f$); (b) at medium and high pressures ($\nu > f$)

This motion has three remarkable properties:

(a) The velocity is in quadrature with the force acting on the electron. As a result, the electron does not absorb any energy at all from the HF field. An electron of the gas behaves exactly as if it were in the middle of a dielectric medium without any losses.

(b) The amplitude of the sinusoidal component of the motion varies with $1/f^2$ where $f = \omega/2\pi$ is the frequency of the field. This phenomenon is obviously due to the inertia of the electron.

(c) If the electric field has a phase θ which differs from π/a, it imparts to the electron a mean velocity $e\, E_0 \cos \theta/m\omega$ (in addition to v_0). Note that this velocity is generally small: 3×10^8 cm/sec for $E_0 = 30$ V/cm, $f = 10$ Mc/s and $\theta = 0$, while an energy of only a few electron-volts corresponds to 10^8 cm/sec. All these considerations are valid as long as an electron has little chance of meeting another particle during one period of the HF field $(\nu \ll f)$.

15.2.2 In a very dense gas

When a gas is present, the motion of an electron is perturbed by collisions with the molecules. If the electric field were continuous, the electron would, in the steady state, have a constant drift velocity which, under certain conditions (see Chapter 9), can be written

$$\mathbf{v} = \mu\, \mathbf{E}$$

where μ is the mobility of the electrons.

We have seen that $\mu \approx e\lambda/m\overline{w}$. The normal practice is to introduce the frequency ν with which the electron undergoes collisions with the molecules of the gas $\nu \approx \overline{w}/\lambda$ and consequently $\mu \approx e/m\nu$.

Let us assume that the concept of mobility is still applicable at HF. This assumes, among other things, that the electron undergoes several collisions during a period $(\nu \gg f)$ so that it is practically in equilibrium with the field at any instant.

The equation for the "mean" motion of an electron (or for the motion of a whole cloud of electrons in the gas) becomes

$$v = \dot{x} = \mu\, E_0 \sin{(\omega t + \theta)} = \frac{e\, E_0}{m\nu} \sin{(\omega t + \theta)} \tag{15.3}$$

and, by integrating,

$$x = x_0 - \frac{\mu\, E_0}{\omega} \cos{(\omega t + \theta)} = x_0 - \frac{e\, E_0}{m\omega\nu} \cos{(\omega t + \theta)} \tag{15.4}$$

Since the velocity is in phase with the force acting, the electron absorbs a mean power

$$\overline{P} = \overline{vF} = \mu\, e\, E_0^2/2 = e^2 E_0^2/2\, m\nu$$

This time the gas of electrons behaves like a resistive metal. The energy it gains from the field is subsequently lost to the ambient gas which it heats.

15.2.3 In a low-density ambient gas $(\nu \lesssim f)$

In the intermediate case, the frequency of collisions is too great to be neglected but not large enough for the drift velocity defined by the mobility to be reached in a much shorter time than the

HF period. Under these conditions, it can be assumed that the action of the collisions is equivalent to that of a frictional force proportional to the mean velocity of the electron:

$$F = -gv$$

The absorption parameter g can be calculated by means of the following simplified reasoning: in the steady state, as the acceleration is zero, the frictional force should be equal and opposite to the attraction of the electric field:

$$F = -eE$$

Hence $g = e/\mu \approx m\nu$.

The equation of motion becomes

$$m\,v = eE_0 \sin(\omega t + \theta) - m\,\nu\,v$$

the solution to which is

$$v = \frac{e\,E_0}{m\,\sqrt{\omega^2 + \nu^2}} \sin(\omega t + \theta - \varphi) \qquad (15.5)$$

where

$$\varphi = \arctan(\omega/\nu)$$

and

$$x = x_0 - \frac{e\,E_0}{\omega m\,\sqrt{\omega^2 + \nu^2}} \cos(\omega t + \theta - \varphi) \qquad (15.6)$$

The mean power absorbed by an electron is then:

$$\overline{P} = \frac{e^2\,E_0^2}{2\,m\,\sqrt{\omega^2 + \nu^2}} \cos\varphi = \frac{e^2\,E_0^2}{2\,m} \cdot \frac{\nu}{(\omega^2 + \nu^2)}$$

The electron gas behaves as if it were in a dielectric medium with a power factor equal to $\cos\varphi$ (loss angle $= \pi/2 - \varphi$). In the steady state, the electrons give up the absorbed power to the molecules of the ambient gas.

The results of Section 15.2.1 and 15.2.2 can be verified by putting $\nu/\omega \ll 1$ and $\gg 1$ respectively in the results in the present section.

Remarks

1. The above analysis can be applied to heavy ions and it then shows that these may be considered as fixed with respect to the electrons because of their large mass.

2. When the whole motion of a cloud of electrons or of heavy ions is under consideration, diffusion of concentration should not be forgotten (see Chapter 8).

3. In all of the above, interactions between electric charges have been neglected since the densities are, in general, small.

15.3 Parameters determining high-frequency breakdown

From the above it follows that the condition for breakdown should be expressed as a relation between:

(a) the breakdown electric field E_c;

(b) its frequency $f = c/\lambda$, where c = velocity of light and λ = wavelength in vacuum;

(c) the pressure of the gas: p, or the m.f.p., l, of the electrons, or the frequency, $\nu = \bar{w}/l$, of their collisions with molecules of the ambient gas ($\bar{w}$ = mean thermal velocity of the electrons);

(d) the dimensions of the enclosure, that is to say, in the particular simple case of a plane, parallel electrodes, the distance d between these electrodes.

It can be seen intuitively that the breakdown field depends on the relative values of l, λ and d, that is to say, the ratios d/l (or pd) and λ/l (or $p\lambda$).

Considerations from dimensional analysis as well as experimental results lead to a condition for breakdown in the form:

$$E_c d = \psi (p\lambda, pd)$$ (15.7)

which is reminiscent of Paschen's law for continuous current.

This relation is represented by a surface in three-dimensional space with coordinates $p\lambda$, pd and $V_c = E_c d$. We shall now investigate the most characteristic parts of this surface.

15.4 Breakdown at very low pressures (secondary electron resonance or "multifactor" effect; $l > d$)

In general, this inequality is satisfied for $p < 10^{-2}$ mm Hg. Under these conditions, the collisions of electrons with the walls or the electrodes are more frequent than those with the molecules of the gas.

Their motion is governed by the equations in Section 15.2.1.

15.4.1 Experimental results

(a) Breakdown takes place at very low voltages, of the order of 100 V.

(b) It depends essentially on the nature of the electrodes or the electrodes or the walls (if the electrodes are outside the enclosure) and not on the nature of the gas or its pressure.

(c) There is a cutoff frequency, f_c, below which it is impossible to initiate a discharge

$$f_c = C/d \qquad (15.8)$$

where

$$C \approx 80 \text{ Mc/s} \cdot \text{cm}$$

(d) When the electrodes are inside the enclosure, there are two values of the breakdown voltage for each value of the frequency. Outside the interval defined by these two values it is impossible either to initiate or to maintain a discharge (unshaded area in Fig. 15.3).

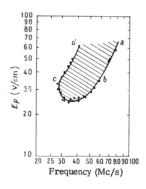

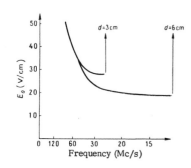

Fig. 15.3. Multifactor effect in hydrogen at 10^{-4} mm Hg (electrodes Ag-Cu, separated by 3 cm and inside the tube). (A. J. HATCH and H. B. WILLIAMS, *J. Appl. Phys.*, **25**, 417, 1954)

Fig. 15.4. HF breakdown in a glass enclosure with plane outer electrodes separated by d cm. Gas: hydrogen at 10^{-3} mm Hg. (E. W. GILL and A. von ENGEL, *Proc. Roy. Soc.*, **A 192**, 446, 1948)

15.4.2 Interpretation

The theory of secondary electron resonance is based on the idea that an avalanche of electrons can only develop if:

(a) the time for electrons to travel from one end of the discharge tube to the other (in a direction parallel to E) is approximately a half-period, $1/2f$, of the HF field; such that the possible secondary electrons in turn leave with the phase necessary for them to be accelerated by the field. There is a sort of resonance between the field and the motion of the electrons;

(b) the field imparts energy to the electrons such that when they strike the electrodes or the walls each one extracts, on the average, at least one secondary electron.

The experimental results can be explained by clarifying and combining these two conditions.

15.5 Breakdown at moderate and high pressures $(l < d)$

At pressures higher than about 10^{-2} mm Hg, there are two cases to be considered with normal enclosures depending on whether the peak amplitude $\hat{x}$ of the oscillations of the electrons is smaller or larger than the dimensions of the enclosure. We have already seen that this amplitude is proportional to $eE_0/m\omega\nu$ or $eE_0/m\omega^2$ depending on whether $\nu \gg \omega$ or $\nu \ll \omega$.

If $\hat{x} > d$, the cloud of electrons is displaced due to the effect of the electric field and strikes the walls twice in each period. The walls therefore play a large part in the breakdown.

If $\hat{x} < d$, conversely, the ionization is localized in the gas while charge is lost essentially due to diffusion towards the walls (attachment and recombination are in general negligible). This is said to be a state of diffusion. This type of discharge, as can be seen, is the simplest, so we shall commence with it.

15.5.1 Diffusion regime $(\hat{x} < d)$

Breakdown takes place at a field E_c such that each electron produces, on the average, at least one pair of ions in the course of its oscillatory motion before disappearing due to diffusion.

The experimental results can be explained by simple physical arguments.

Thus, when the dimensions of the receptacle and the distance between the electrodes increase, the lifetime of an electron leaving the center is longer and it has more chances of ionizing the gas before disappearing.

The breakdown voltage is reduced. This can be seen from Fig. 15.5.

A minimum depending on p can also be seen as in the case of Paschen's curves.

Referring back to Section 15.2.3, it can in fact be seen that the energy absorbed by the electrons passes through a maximum at $\nu = \omega$. It can be verified that this value of ν corresponds well with the minimum pressure of the present curves.

Note: In enclosures with very small dimensions when the pressure is low (< 1 mm Hg), it is possible that the reduction in the total ionization results not from the velocity of the electrons getting out of phase with the HF electric field as above, but from acceleration of the diffusion so that the electrons can no longer ionize many molecules before disappearing at the walls.

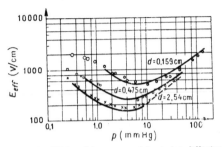

Fig. 15.5. HF breakdown potentials under diffusion conditions. Gas: hydrogen. f = 3000 Mc/s. (S. C. BROWN, *Hnb. d. Phys.*, **22**, Springer, 1956)

15.5.2 High pressure and large amplitude regime $(\hat{x} > d)$

This condition may be brought about by reducing the frequency (Section 15.2.3) or by decreasing the dimensions of the enclosure.

Figure 15.6 represents some experimental results characteristic of this type of discharge.

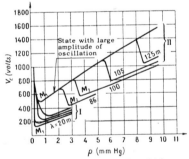

Fig. 15.6. Breakdown potentials at high pressure and large oscillation amplitudes. (G. W. GILL and R. H. DONALDSON, *Phil. Mag.*, **12**, 719, 1931)

The curves of type I (high frequencies) have only one minimum (M_1) and characterize a diffusion state as above $(\hat{x} < d)$.

The curves of type II (lower frequencies) also have a minimum of type M_2 which is explained in the following manner:

At high pressures, ν is so large that $\hat{x} < d$ and there is still a state of diffusion. But when the pressure decreases, the amplitude increases with $E_0/\omega\nu$ or $E_0/\omega p$, and there comes a moment when the cloud of oscillating electrons periodically comes in contact with the walls and loses a large number of its particles. The total amount of ionization therefore decreases sharply while V_c rises rapidly.

At a given pressure, the cutoff frequency is that below which the diffusion state gives way to the state of high-amplitude oscillations. It is characterized by a discontinuity in V_c. It is naturally higher the lower the pressure (Fig. 15.7).

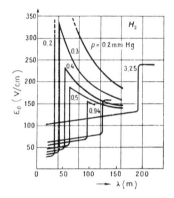

Fig. 15.7. Variations in the cutoff frequency with wavelength. Gas: hydrogen H_2. (W. B. GILL and A. von ENGEL, *Proc. Roy. Soc.*, **A 197**, 107, 1949)

REFERENCES

S. C. BROWN, *Basic Data of Plasma Physics* (J. Wiley, 1960).
G. FRANCIS, *Ionization Phenomena in Gases* (Butterworth, 1960).

16 diagnostics

As in all sciences, methods and instruments for observation play an essential part in the physics of plasmas* and gaseous discharges. It seems that nowhere else does one find such an abundance and variety. This is no doubt due to the diversity and complexity of the phenomena to be investigated, and to their sensitivity to intervention by the experimenter. As a result, none of the methods is either perfect or universal; their proliferation is in itself a sign of weakness. Progress has still to be made in this field, which is called diagnostics.

16.1 The object of the investigation

Generally the "unknowns" to be determined are the nature of the particles, their density, their energy or their velocity, the frequency of their collisions, the electric and magnetic fields, and finally the energy transfers of various forms (thermal, radiative, electric, etc.).

This chapter is devoted to a brief review of diagnostic methods. Appendices I and II deal in more detail with Langmuir's probe and microwave diagnostics.

---

*Editor's Footnote: The term plasma was originally introduced to describe the state in the positive column of a discharge but today is universally employed as a synonym for "ionized gas." (See Section 12.2.5.2.)

16.2 Nature of the particles

The nature of the particles means both their chemical and their physical nature: ionized or nonionized atom or molecule, electron or neutron. Photons are here considered to be particles.

16.2.1 Optical spectroscopy [1]

This is one of the most powerful and widely used methods. Although experimental discharges are usually produced in pure gases, or at the most binary mixtures, the constituents of which are known, the inevitable walls as well as oil from the vacuum pumps introduce impurities which cannot be neglected and the nature and concentration of which it is important to know. By comparing the optical spectra of a discharge with standard spectra, it is possible to determine the wavelength of the lines observed. Double-entry reference books (giving lengths and emitters) then give the chemical nature of the emitters and their degree of ionization. The intensity of the lines indicates their concentration.

This method is called emission spectroscopy.

Sometimes the discharge is irradiated with polychromatic radiation and the degree of absorption of the characteristic lines is observed. This is absorption spectroscopy.

Absorption spectroscopy (and also emission spectroscopy) does not notably perturb the discharge under observation. This is one of the great advantages of these methods.

Observations can be made outside the visible range and now extend to the far I. R. (infrared) (wavelength of several hundreds of microns; characteristic molecular spectra) and U.V. (ultraviolet) (atomic spectra of light bodies or of a high order) and even to X-rays.

However, this extension is only made at the expense of more complicated apparatus. Thus, outside the visible region it is difficult to use photographic plates. For U. V. radiation scintillators are used in conjunction with photomultipliers, and for I. R., semiconducting cells (cf. photoelectric cells: photovoltaic or photoresistive).

It is imperative to use electric detectors when it is desired to record the evolution of a spectrum with time.

Since U. V. radiation is absorbed by atmospheric air and normal glass, U. V. spectrographs do not usually contain any lenses or prisms but employ diffraction gratings operating by reflection in vacuum.

Even when a spectrum has been obtained under good conditions, there may still be difficulties of identification. On the one hand, there are still gaps in the reference tables; and, on the other hand, the resolving power of the spectrographs may not be sufficient.

Another limitation of the spectroscopic method appears when it is applied to the study of very hot gases. Due to ionization, their atoms tend to lose all their electrons and consequently their capacity to radiate with the characteristic wavelengths. Very hot gases are not very luminous.

16.2.2 Mass spectroscopy

Mass spectroscopy using electric deflection gives q/mv^2, where q, m and v are respectively the charge, mass and velocity of the particle. With magnetic deflection q/mv can be found. With crossed electric and magnetic fields, q/m and v can be found separately (J. J. Thomson's method of parabolas). To determine q and m the spectrograph has to be combined with another instrument such as, for example, a scintillator producing a signal the intensity of which varies with the mass of the incident particle (see Section 16.2.3).

When the number of particles to be observed is very small, they cannot be measured directly with a galvanometer or even with an electron amplifier. An electron multiplier [2] is then used which is merely a photomultiplier without a photocathode, and which has the added advantage of having a fairly short response time. Using this apparatus it is possible to count electrons and also heavy particles, but with a rather small efficiency.

16.2.3 Scintillators [3]

Scintillators tend to supplant any other form of radiation detector in the field of nuclear physics. As we have seen in Sections 16.2.1 and 16.2.2, scintillators emit a luminous pulse under impact from particles of matter or photons. The amplitude and duration of this pulse varies with the nature of the incident particle and of the material making up the scintillator. The luminous pulse is converted by a photomultiplier into an electric pulse which can be handled (i.e., measured, followed in time, recorded) more easily.

16.2.4 Semiconductors [4]

When a semiconductor is submitted to particle or photon radiation in the presence of a magnetic field, a variation in the electrical conductivity or an E.M.F. can be observed. This galvanomagnetic effect forms the basis of a certain number of radiation detectors. Other semiconductor detectors rely on the effect of particles on p-n junctions.

16.2.5 Photographic plates [5]

A photographic impression is made on a plate to a greater or lesser extent by all charged particles and not only by photons. The nature and energy of a charged particle can be determined by following its trajectory in the developed plate as shown by a track of black grains, particularly if the plate was placed in a magnetic field during the experiment.

A difficulty often encountered in trying to study particles of matter with photographic plates is that of preventing light from the discharge making an impression on the plates.

16.3 Particle density

16.3.1 Neutral particles

At a given temperature, the particle density is proportional to their pressure. Now in most gaseous discharges, the temperature of the neutral ambient gas is that of the laboratory. To find the density it is therefore sufficient to measure the pressure with ordinary manometers. The most widely used are ionization gauges and thermal conductivity gauges (see vacuum techniques) which cover a very wide range of pressures: 10^{-10} to 10^2 mm Hg, which correspond to particle densities from 3.10^6 to 3.10^{18} cm^{-3}.

The great inconvenience of gauges of this type is the following— they are generally fixed to the walls of the enclosure where the discharge is taking place by means of a narrow tube of varying size. To be precise, they only indicate the pressure of the gas which they enclose and not that prevailing in the discharge proper. In practice, this is of no importance in the steady state, but it can be in a transitory state when the pressure is not uniform throughout the enclosure.

Another inconvenience is that the response time of thermal gauges is fairly long, as is that of ionization gauges at very low pressures ($\sim$ 1 msec).

Moreover, an ionization gauge is extremely sensitive to the magnetic fields present in almost all plasmas.

Another type of gauge has appeared more recently: the piezo-electric gauge which converts pressure to electric voltage. It is in principle more adaptable than the others but only operates at fairly high pressures.

16.3.2 Charged particles

(A)*Langmuir's probe or electrostatic probe.* For a long time this apparatus was the plasma physicist's favorite. With this it is possible to determine the density of ions and electrons and the temperature of the latter. We shall study it in detail in Appendix I.

(B) *Microwave interferometry.*

(C) *Microwave cavities.* Since the end of the last war these two methods have been expanded with the development of the techniques of centimetric and millimetric waves. They will also be dealt with in an appendix.

(D) *Stark effect.* The structure of the spectral lines depends on the conditions under which they are emitted. In particular, in the presence of a powerful, uniform electric field, they are split into several less intense lines, the degree of splitting depending on the strength of the field. If the latter is not homogeneous, the splitting is not the same for all atoms. The result is a single line which is wider than the initial characteristic line. This is exactly what happens if the density of the ions and electrons is very high ($> 10^{13}$ cm^{-3}): their microscopic field is then sufficient to cause a Stark effect. The number of lines of the same spectral series which overlap increases with the particle density, particularly at the limit of the series where the lines are always very close. The number of lines which can still be distinguished is therefore a measure of the density [6].

16.3.3 Particle beams

Section 16.3.2 (B), (C) and (D) also apply to beams of particles. The intensity of a beam of particles can be measured equally well by counting the number of pulses from a suitable detector (scintillator, semiconductor, etc.) placed in its path. This method is valid for neutral or charged particles provided that the intensity of the beam is not too high.

If the particles have a fairly high energy, then the secondary emission of electrons from a target bombarded by the beam can be measured; but this depends on the nature of the particles being investigated as well as their velocity.

Note: The study of the frequencies and intensities of spectral lines (Section 16.2.1) applies to neutral particles as well as charged particles, in a beam or in statistical equilibrium.

16.4 Velocity or energy

A distinction must be made between the directional or drift velocity and that due to diffusion and the random velocity characteristic of thermal agitation.

16.4.1 Directional velocity

(A) *Doppler effect.* When an atom moves with a velocity v with respect to the laboratory coordinate system, the apparent wavelength of the spectral lines is modified in the ratio $[1 + (v/c) \cos \theta]$ where θ is the angle between the velocity v and the direction of observation of the radiation. Any motion of the assembly of neutral or partially ionized atoms is therefore seen as a displacement of the spectral lines. This phenomenon is used a great deal in the study of shock waves and plasma instabilities.

(B) *Mass spectrography* (see Section 16.2.2).

(C) *Variable potential collector.* Faraday cylinder. The collector is placed behind a grid or collimator which defines the direction of the particles under investigation and which is raised to the potential of the enclosure which is taken as origin. If the potential of the collector is V, it will not collect any particles with an energy lower than $q\,V$. By varying V it is possible to determine the energy spectrum of the particles of charge q, and in particular their overall velocity.

When using this method, it is essential that reflection and secondary emission from the collector be eliminated since these would falsify the measurements; usually the collector is made in the form of a cavity so that the primary and secondary particles are reflected several times before they can escape. It is also possible to place a grid immediately in front of the collector and raise it to a negative potential sufficient to repulse secondary electrons.

(D) *Time of flight method.* Using scintillators and photomultipliers (for example), particles may be detected at two widely separated points in their trajectory. Knowing the distance between these two points and the time elapsing between detection at one and at the other, the velocity of the particles can be deduced.

(E) *Calorimetric and mechanical measurements.* A target introduced into a beam of particles of matter is raised to a temperature which depends on the kinetic energy of these particles. Knowing the number and mass of the latter and the temperature of the target, the velocity can be determined. The target should preferably be made of some refractory material (molybdenum, tungsten or tantalum). The temperature is measured by a thermocouple or an optical pyrometer. The deflection of a ballistic pendulum under the impact of the beam can also be found from which the total momentum can be calculated.

(F) *Absorbent screens.* A widely used method is to place absorbent screens of increasing thickness in front of a suitable detector until the particles under investigation disappear entirely; in this way their energy spectrum can be found.

(G) *Scintillators.* The intensity of light emitted by a scintillation counter (Section 16.2.3) depends in general on the energy of

N

the particle which excites it. This fact can be used as the basis for measuring the energy spectrum of a beam of particles. However, the relation between the luminous intensity and the energy of a particle has first to be found as this relation may not be linear. In practice, spectra are studied by means of a multichannel analyzer known as a pulse height analyzer or "kicksorter." This is an electronic device which indicates the number of pulses received in a given time and with an amplitude within a given range determined by the channel width, this being done for several ranges simultaneously.

(H) *Photographic plates* (see Section 16.2.5).

(L) *X-ray emission* [7]. The energy of a fast beam of electrons can be deduced by observation of the X-rays to which it gives rise when incident on a target (generally tungsten).

16.4.2 Random velocities (or temperature)

(A) *Broadening of spectral lines.* In this case the Doppler effect has a different amplitude and direction for each particle. When the law for the velocity distribution is Maxwellian, the lines become broadened while retaining their symmetric bell shape. The mean square velocity of the particles can be deduced from the line width. Other spectroscopic methods can also be used [8].

(B) *Langmuir's probe* (see Appendix I).

(C) *Electromagnetic emission* (see Appendix II).

16.5 Electric field

16.5.1 Langmuir's probe (see Appendix I)

16.5.2 Beams of electrons [9]

The deflection of a beam of electrons when passing through an electric field indicates the magnitude of the field. In this way the electric field along a discharge could be measured.

16.6 Magnetic field

16.6.1 Magnetic probe [10]

This is the most widely used instrument. It consists of one or more bobbins with several turns of wire and mounted in a glass or quartz rod: the p.d. at the ends of each bobbin is proportional to the time derivative of the magnetic flux.

16.6.2 Hall-effect probe [11]

This probe consists of a plate of semiconducting material through which an electric current is passed in a direction parallel to the long face. When the probe is placed in a magnetic field, an E.M.F. appears at the ends of a segment parallel to the long face and perpendicular to the current. This E.M.F. is proportional to the component of the magnetic field perpendicular to the long face.

REFERENCES

1. S. S. PENNER, *Quantitative Molecular Spectroscopy and Gas Emissivity* (A. Wesley, 1959).
   C. A. MOORE, *Multiplet Table of Astrophysical Interest* (NBS, Note 36, 1959).
   G. R. HARRISON, *Wavelength Table* (J. Wiley,(1956).
   H. WULF, *Plasma Diagnostics by Spectroscopic Means* (Nucl. Instr. and Methods, 4, 352, 1959).
2. F. H. COENGSEN and F. C. FORD, *Pyrotron Plasma Heating Experiments* (2nd Geneva Conference, No. 15/378, 1958).
   H. W. BANDEL, *Space Charge Effects in Ion Energy Analyzer* (Plasma Physics Meeting, Monterey, Calif., No. F 12, Dec. 1959).
3. *Scintillation Counter Symposium*, IRE Trans. NS-5, 3,1958.
4. L. KOCH, *Detection of Nuclear Radiation by Means of Semiconductors* (Onde électrique, 40, Nov. 1960).
5. W. M. JONES et al., *Nuclear Plate Cameras for the Measurement of Proton Energies* (Nucl. Instr. and Methods, 5, 327-331, 1959).
   C. F. POWELL et al., *The Study of Elementary Particles by Photographic Methods* (Pergamon, 1959).
6. INGLIS and TELLER, *Series Limit Spectra* (Astroph. Journ, 9, 439, 1939).
7. A. GIBSON, *Tungsten Probe Experiment* (Harwell Memo, 64, Nov. 1959).
8. Anonymous, *Proc. of Sympos. on Spectroscopic Measurement of High Temperature* (Chicago, March 1960).
   W. BARR and R. KELLEY, *Spectroscopic Measurement in P-4* (Monterey Meeting, No. D 7, Dec. 1959).
   G. JURGENS, Z. Phys. (134, 21, 1952).
   R. W. LARENZ, Z. Phys. (129, 327 and 343, 1951).
   W. LOCHTE-HOLTGREVEN, *Production and Measurement of High Temperature* (Reports on Progress in Physics, London, 1958).

9. D. GABOR et al., *Langmuir Paradox* (Nature, 176, 916, Nov. 1955).

   T. I. PASSELL, *Ion Beam Space Potential Measurement with Electron Beam* (Monterey Meeting, No. F 15, Dec. 1959).

10. LOVBERG, *The Use of Magnetic Probes in Plasma Diagnostics* (Ann. of Phys., 8, 3 and 311-323, 1959).

11. Anon., *Solid State Physics* (Vol. 5, 1960).

See also: KONSTANTINOV, B. P., *Diagnostika plazmy*, Gosatomizdat, Moscow (1963).

APPENDIX I

electrostatic or langmuir probes

A plasma theoretically behaves as a perfect conductor of continuous currents; it is therefore at a uniform potential. Let us call its potential V_p. Let us introduce into the plasma a plane metal electrode S (probe, Fig. I.1) of area A and let us raise it to a potential V with respect to another metal electrode M of large dimensions and also in contact with the plasma (this can be the walls of the enclosure if they are metal). If V is varied, S receives a current I of the form shown in Fig. I.2.

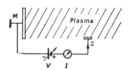

Fig. I.1. Langmuir probe

When V is highly negative (region A), the electrons are practically all repulsed and none of them can fall on the probe. On the other hand, the positive ions are attracted by it and form a positive space charge of thickness d (transition sheath) on its surface. This is a kind of diode, the emissive electrode being the plasma and the other electrode the probe S. All the ions which, by virtue of their energy of thermal agitation, cross the boundary F of the plasma in the direction of S reach the probe which therefore receives per unit of surface a saturation ion current of:

$$I_{is} = A\,j_{is} = -\frac{n_i\,\bar{w}_i}{4}\,A\,e \qquad (\text{I.1})$$

where $n_i = n_e$ is the charge density in the plasma and $\bar{w}_i$ is the mean of the velocity distribution for the ions which is assumed to be Maxwellian. This obviously assumes that the thickness of the sheath is very much smaller than both the linear dimensions of S (to avoid edge effect) and the m.f.p. of the ions in the ambient gas (to avoid deflecting collisions).

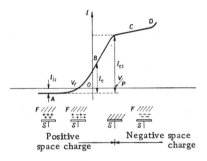

Fig. I.2. Langmuir probe characteristic

Under these conditions, the thickness of the sheath is given by the theory of the space charge limited diode

$$|j_{is}| = \frac{1}{9\,\pi}\left(\frac{2\,e}{m_i}\right)^{1/2}\frac{|V_s|^{3/2}}{d^2} \quad (\text{CGS ESU}) \qquad (\text{I.2})$$

where $V_s = V - V_p$, assuming that the energy of thermal agitation of the ions is small in comparison with the potential energy which is imparted to them by the probe. The sheath cannot usually be seen with the naked eye since there are no electrons in this region and there are no radiative recombinations or excitations by collisions and therefore the sheath does not emit light.

Experiment shows that, for a given plasma, $\tilde{d} \propto |V_s|^{3/4}$ which confirms the theory sketched above.

As V increases, the probe collects more and more electrons. Since it always collects the same number of ions, the resultant current (algebraically) is

$$I = I_{is} + I_e$$

The transition sheath is filled with more and more electrons. But, because of the retarding potential of the probe $(V < V_p)$, only a fraction f_e of the electrons which, by virtue of their thermal agitation, cross the boundary F of the plasma in the direction of S actually reach S. This fraction is given (see Section 7.3) by

$$f_e = \exp(eV_s/kT_e) = \exp(eV/kT_e) \cdot \exp(-eV_p/kT_e)$$

where T_e is the thermodynamic temperature of the electrons. The electron current of the probe will then be

$$I_e = A\, j_e = f_e\, \tfrac{1}{4}\, n_e\, \overline{w}_e\, A\, e \propto \exp(eV/kT_e)$$

As a result, if the velocity distribution for the electrons is in fact Maxwellian, part B of the characteristic of the probe should have an exponential form and the temperatures of the electrons could be deduced from the relation

$$\boxed{\dfrac{d(\ln I_e)}{dV} = \dfrac{e}{kT_e}} \tag{I.3}$$

If the ordinates I are transferred to a logarithmic scale, the slope of the straight line obtained will give T_e.

When $V = V_f$, $I_e = -I_{is}$ and $I = 0$; this is the point of floating potential: the probe behaves as an insulator.

The point $V = 0$ has no particular significance; its position depends on the reference electrode chosen (M in this case).

As V increases once more, there comes a moment when the characteristic inflects sharply $(V = V_p)$. At this point the probe has the same potential as the plasma. The boundary F coincides with S and the probe collects as many electrons or ions as pass through any imaginary surface, of the same area, in the plasma which is assumed to be homogeneous. The electron current is then given by

$$I_{es} = \tfrac{1}{4}\, n_e\, \overline{w}_e\, Ae = n_e\, (kT_e/2\pi\, m_e)^{1/2}\, Ae \tag{I.4}$$

I_{es} can easily be found from the characteristic and, knowing A and T_e, $n_e\,(= n_i)$ can hence be deduced. On the other hand, it is more difficult to determine V_p since the "knee" in the characteristic is not always very pronounced.

Knowing n_i and I_{is}, $\overline{w}_i$ can be found from (I.1) and hence T_i is known.

It can also be shown that

$$\boxed{I_{is} \approx 0.4\, A e n_i\, (2\, kT_e/m_i)^{1/2}} \tag{I.5}$$

Note that, even if $T_i = T_e$, $I_{is} \ll I_{es}$ since the ions are much heavier than the electrons. Besides, in most common discharges $T_i < T_e$ which accentuates the difference still more.

As V increases beyond V_p, the number of ions which can reach the probe decreases and I increases slightly.

I rises steeply for very high potentials V (region D): this is because the electrons are accelerated by the field to such a degree that they are able to ionize the remaining gas and multiply rapidly (see Chapter 11).

The above is only valid provided the probe does not significantly perturb the plasma. This implies that the probe should be small and that the potential applied to it should not be too large.

Finally, the presence of a magnetic field can greatly complicate interpretation of the probe characteristic. In fact, if the magnetic field is intense enough, the m.f.p. of the electrons is greatly reduced, and their diffusion towards the probe no longer obeys a law of the type (I.4). However, it would appear from experimental results that relation (I.3) remains valid. Since the m.f.p. of the ions is modified very greatly by the magnetic field $(m_i \gg m_e)$, the value of T_e given by (I.3) can be substituted in (I.5) and $n_e = n_i$ can be deduced.

In practice, probes in the form of wires of small diameter (a few tens of mm) are used. They give results analogous to those for plane probes. Only the numerical factors of some of the relations are modified to take account of the new geometry.

Balanced probes as shown schematically in Fig. I.3 are also used, the characteristics being of the form shown in Fig. I.4. Reasoning analogous to the above leads to the expression

$$\frac{d}{dV}\left[\ln\left(\frac{I_{es1} + I_{es2}}{I_{e2}} - 1\right)\right] = -\frac{e}{kT_e} \tag{I.6}$$

where T_e can be obtained. Equation (I.5) then gives n_i which is equal to n_e.

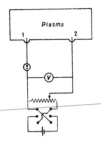

Fig. I.3. Balanced probe device

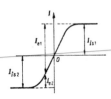

Fig. I.4. Characteristic for balanced probe

The advantage of this device is that the total current traversing the plasma and the exterior circuit never exceed I_{is_1} or I_{is_2} which are always smaller than I_{es}.

Besides any perturbation they may cause in the plasma, all the probes have the great disadvantage that they evaporate or even melt rapidly in very dense or hot plasmas.

The readings they give are also falsified by secondary emission when they are bombarded by electrons or X- or U.V. rays.

REFERENCES

1. I. LANGMUIR and H. MOTT-SMITH, *General Electric Review*, (27 , pp. 449, 538, 616, 762, 810, 1924). *Phys. Rev.* (2nd series, 28, 727, 1926).
2. A. GUTHRIE and R. K. WAKERLING, *The Characteristics of Electric Discharges in Magnetic Fields* (McGraw-Hill, 1949).
3. E. O. JOHNSON and L. MALTER, *Phys. Rev.* (80, 58, 1950).
4. V. I. PISTONOVICH, *Plasma Physics and the Problem of Controlled Thermonuclear Reactions* (Pergamon, Vol. IV, 1960).

APPENDIX II

plasma diagnostics by microwave methods

The interaction between plasma and radiation provides new methods of plasma diagnostics.

The plasma in effect behaves like a dissipative dielectric (because of collisions) and radiative dielectric (because of its temperature). Its complex dielectric constant and its emissive power depend among other things on the densities of charged and neutral particles as well as their temperature. Hence the following diagnostic methods.

II.1 Cavity resonator method [1 to 4]

The plasma occupies the axial region of a coaxial cavity or the central region of a spherical cavity. The resonance frequency and the Q factor of the cavity differ from the values they have when the plasma is not present. From this difference and the known distribution of the field in the cavity, the density of plasma and its temperature can be deduced by means of a hypothesis as to its spatial distribution.

However, it is not always possible to construct a cavity which will give the required information without perturbing the plasma under investigation.

II.2 Method using electromagnetic beam [2], [3], [5]

In general, the frequency of collisions between the electron and other particles of the plasma is small compared with the critical plasma frequency f_p defined by:

$$f_p = (n_e e / \pi \, m_e)^{1/2} \quad \text{(CGS ESU)} \tag{II.1}$$

As a result, in the absence of a magnetic field, the refractive index of the plasma for a wave of frequency f is:

$$\mu \approx \sqrt{1 - (f_p/f)^2} \tag{II.2}$$

This relation is still valid in the presence of a magnetostatic field provided that the latter is parallel to the electric vector of the wave.

For $f > f_p$, the plasma behaves as a dielectric with refractive index $0 < \mu < 1$; for $f < f_p$, the refractive index is negative and the wave can no longer be propagated in the plasma. At these frequencies, the latter can only support evanescent waves which are heavily attenuated. When $f = f_p$, there is said to be cutoff. If the cutoff frequency f_p can be determined (for example, by varying f and observing the wave transmitted through the plasma), the maximum local density of electrons encountered by the wave can be calculated from (II.1).

Unfortunately, actual techniques are such that it is not possible to vary f continuously in the range 1 to 300 Gc/s ($\lambda_0 = 30$ cm to 1 mm) where most plasma cutoff frequencies are situated. The only instruments available in this range operate in a discrete number of narrow bands. Thus it is usually only possible to determine the interval in which the frequency must lie; however, the maximum electron density of the plasma can be found from this.

Another method consists in using a two-beam interferometer into which the region of the plasma to be investigated may be inserted (Fig. II.1).

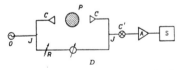

Fig. II.1. Microwave interferometer. O—Oscillator; J—hybrid junction; C—horn; R—variable attenuator; D—variable phase shifter; C'—crystal detector; A—amplifier; S—oscilloscope; P—cross section of plasma under investigation

The presence of the plasma reduces the optical path $(\Sigma \mu l)$ of the corresponding wave $(\cdot \mu < 1)$. The interferometer gives the resultant path difference and from this the mean density of electrons along the path of the wave can be calculated.

Finally, information about a column of plasma can be obtained by irradiating it in a transverse direction with a plane microwave beam and observing the diffraction which occurs as a result.

II.3 Plasma radiation [6]

Close to its critical frequency, f_p, a plasma radiates more or less like a black body. It can be shown that this radiation is analogous to the thermal noise familiar to radio-engineers; the intensity may be expressed by

$$P = C \, T_e \cdot \Delta f \tag{II.3}$$

where C is a constant, T_e the temperature of the electrons in the plasma and Δf the frequency band admitted by the receiver employed. In general, P is determined by comparison with a standard noise source which can be substituted for the plasma under investigation.

II.4

All these methods of measurement are somewhat inexact and the last (Section II.3) can only give qualitative indications. However, microwave methods are of great value today, since: a) the other possible methods are no more precise; b) the perturbation due to microwaves is usually negligible; c) the small time constant of semiconductor microwave detectors makes good time resolution possible.

REFERENCES

1. S. C. BROWN, et al., *Trans. Inst. Radio Eng.*, MTT, 69 (1959). *Phys. of Fluids*, 3 (5), 806 (1960).
2. V. E. GOLANT, *Sov. Phys.-Tech. Phys.*, 5 (11), 1197 (1961).
3. T. CONSOLI, *CEA Report*, No. 1703 (1960).
4. K. B. PERSSON, *Phys. Rev.*, 106, 191 (1957).
5. M. A. HEALD, *USAEC Rep.*, MATT-17 (1959).
6. R. PAPOULAR and J. BALAZARD, *Application des ondes hyperfrequences et infrarouges à l'étude des plasmas*, Dunod, 1965.
7. G.BEKEFI and S.C.BROWN, *Am. J. of Phys.*, 29, (7), 404 (1961). F. CABANNES, A. HADNI et al., *Comptes Rendus Acad. Sci.*, 255 (2), 274 (1962).

index